D1259609

DYLAN THOMAS

Early Prose Writings

EDITED WITH AN INTRODUCTION
BY

Walford Davies

SWARTHMORE PUBLIC LIBRARY 62622

LONDON
J. M. DENT & SONS LTD

First published 1971
© The Trustees for the Copyrights of Dylan Thomas, 1971
© Introduction and arrangement, Walford Davies, 1971

All rights reserved. No part of this publication may be reproduced, stored in a retrieval system, or transmitted, in any form or by any means, electronic, mechanical, photocopying, recording or otherwise, without the prior permission of J. M. Dent & Sons Ltd.

Made in Great Britain
at the
Aldine Press · Letchworth · Herts
for
J. M. DENT & SONS LTD
Aldine House · Bedford Street · London

ISBN: 0 460 03990 3

CONTENTS

Part I of this volume contains creative work – short stories and excerpts from an unpublished novel and a film script. Part II contains critical and other writings.

TEXTUAL NOTE

In transcription, minor errors
have been silently corrected.
Some items from newspaper sources
have been re-paragraphed.

ACKNOWLEDGMENTS

To David Higham Associates Ltd for permission to
include copyright material; to the Lockwood Memorial
Library, New York, for permission to include items from
their MS. holdings, and to Mr C. G. Gay, Curator of that
library, for confirming some manuscript readings; to
Lady Pamela Snow for permission to include excerpts
from the poet's early letters to her; to Mrs Edith Capon
for permission to include 'Idioms'; and to Professor Ralph
Maud for bringing the latter to the editor's attention.

INTRODUCTION

There is general agreement with Dylan Thomas's own judgment concerning the relative position of his writing in prose: on the whole, he came to regard his work in this medium as side-issues from his chief concern with poetry. But a survey of his career shows that in the 1930s those side-issues were more organically related to the poetry than at any subsequent period. The bulk of this selection is taken from that decade and, in the field of the short story, represents material which complements the stories in *A Prospect of the Sea*. The correspondence of such material to the central imagination, texture and atmosphere of the early poems is one not to be looked for in the poet's later work. To a large extent, works like *The Doctor and the Devils* or *Under Milk Wood* derived their impetus from the attractions of the media which called them forth. And in addition, the writing of prose had by that time become a necessary means of securing a livelihood in a financially disorganized life.

A help in that direction was also provided, in the 1930s, by the review work Thomas was offered by various editors. This was the beginning of the ever-increasing effect his reputation as a poet was to have in drawing him into the more public world of journals, films and radio. As far as reviewing was concerned, he could often make fun of the effort. Before he started, he said characteristically, in 1933: 'Oh, to be a critic!' "Mr. X shows promise. This week's masterpiece. Mr. Y is bad." So simple, no bother, no bleeding of writing.' At the other end of the decade, he had first-hand knowledge of the strain involved: 'I'm sick of avoiding clichés of appreciation and expressing a large like in small, tough terms.' In the same year (1938), reviewing Beckett's *Murphy*, he showed signs of having matured to his task: 'Mr. Beckett, who is . . . an enemy of obviousness, would hate to be reviewed by the cash-register system that deals in the currency of petty facts and penny praises.' In between, he had earned the description made of him by a member of the *New English Weekly* staff as 'a swell reviewer'. The striking self-assurance of the young poet reviewing Spender's *Vienna* or an edition of the poems of John Clare is outdone only by the younger schoolboy of fifteen casting a surprisingly confident eye over the situation of 'Modern Poetry' in his school magazine. Thomas's reviews were always readable, and they show an intelligent mind registering decisively its main impressions and maintaining its right to intuitive judgment and a sense of fun. Thomas was the sort of person who, in 1937, could sincerely pay this compliment—

> I sometimes think of Mr. Auden's poetry as a hygiene, a knowledge and practice, based on a brilliantly prejudiced analysis of contemporary disorders, relating to the preservation and promotion of health, a sanitary science and a flusher of melancholies. I sometimes think of his poetry as a great war, admire intensely the mature, religious, and logical fighter, and deprecate the boy bushranger.
>
> I think he is a wide and deep poet, and that his first narrow angles, of pedantry and careful obscurity, are worn almost all away. I think he is as technically sufficient, and as potentially productive of greatness, as any poet writing in English. He makes Mr. Yeats's isolation guilty as a trance.

and then round it with a shrewd postscript—

> Congratulations on Auden's seventieth birthday.

The short stories in Part I of this volume, augmenting as they do the prose of *A Prospect of the Sea*, suggest the personality implicit in the poems. The poet's finest achievement in prose—surely his *Portrait of the Artist as a Young Dog* with *Under Milk Wood*—doesn't seem at first intimated in the nature of this early work. In many ways Thomas from 1939 onwards must have seen the *Portrait* stories as a means of breaking the morbid deadlock of his career to date. In 1936 Richard Church asked the poet, 'Why do you not give your attention to a tale of the world where your early years were spent?'—seeking, no doubt, to deflect Thomas from the private nightmare world of his early work. Thomas's reply at the time was still to offer Church, at that time working for Dent's, stories of the kind represented here. He was not at that time temperamentally capable of moving outwards to a more objective, varied world for his material. That movement outwards was to come with the first of the *Portrait* stories, and was to parallel a similar development in the poetry. In this sense, the *Portrait* shows a decided effort of the will. From there on, autobiographical material was to be related to a living world, and the prose started to look outwards and around. Up to that point it had been a very different matter altogether.

The strangeness of some of the earlier stories printed here, such as 'Brember', 'Jarley's' or 'The End of the River', seems simple enough. They exhibit a young and ordinary delight in their basic fictive situations, marked lightly by their elegiac and supernatural flavour. One feels that they just came as useful, if fantastic, ideas to the young writer; that they have a kind of *objective* inventiveness, exhibiting a callow delight in a short plot with the possibility of surprise. But in the majority of the short stories collected here there seems to be an intensity which belies a deeper impulse than merely the urge to complete a story. Imaginative play is made of the demonic, or the merely dark, intimations present in the natural world, in ordinary human relationships or in received myths. The precarious balance between the benignant and the malignant, between a revealed and a concealed nature, or between a Christian and a pagan scheme of things, is common to a great deal going on in Thomas's early imagined world. Queer it may be, but it is something more complex than what Hugh Gordon Porteous once described it as being—'a queer escape-country for the comfort of the overbepoliticked'. Similarly, despite their experimental, violent flavour, the stories cannot be labelled as mere exercises in literary fashions of the time. The sub-literary impulse of the *avant-garde*, daring and perverse in proportion to the complacency it seeks to erode, is not enough to account for the consistency of imagination in this material. Looking at what he had written, Thomas was often doubtful concerning its independent, literary value, referring unequivocally to his early prose as 'dream stories, very mixed, very violent', 'difficult and violent tales'. But there was never, on his part, any real questioning of the actual *taste* involved. Sending Pamela

Hansford Johnson a short story in May 1934, he told her to
ignore the details—'just tell whether, as a whole, it's at all
successful'.

The savage intensity of pieces like 'The Burning Baby' or
'The School for Witches' places them in strict contemporary
relationship to similar stories in *A Prospect of the Sea*. That they
are, however, more intense and arcane than even 'The Visitor'
or 'The Enemies' is what accounts for the fact that, despite
Thomas's efforts, they remained uncollected. In December
1934, when the poet was looking forward to the publication of
18 Poems (published later that month), he was seriously contemplating a collection of stories as well. His main source at
this time would have been his 'Red Notebook' which, apart
from stories like 'The Tree' or 'The Enemies', included four of
the stories collected here. These were 'The True Story', 'The
Vest', 'Gaspar, Melchior, Balthasar' and 'The Burning
Baby'. He had hopes of 'a publisher, probably Spottiswoode,
publishing my stories in the spring' of 1935. That hope was
frustrated. In February 1937, he was still sending them round
to be considered for volume publication. A year later, he was
writing to Charles Fisher to announce that a volume titled *The
Burning Baby: 16 Stories* was to be published the following month
by the Europa Press. The fact that sixteen stories were being
considered at that time means that some of the items collected
here were involved. But a collection as inclusive as Thomas
envisaged did not prove possible. In November 1938 Thomas
had hopes that John Lehmann and the Hogarth Press would
publish a volume, this time titled *In the Direction of the Beginning*.
What actually transpired was that Dent agreed to a selection of
the stories to accompany poems in the prose-verse volume, *The
Map of Love*, published in August 1939.

Writing to David Higham, his literary agent, the poet agreed
to the selection, which was based very much on Richard
Church's judgment. That judgment was perfectly sound, and
Thomas was stating the truth when he described the stories for
The Map of Love as 'the best—especially in a book also to
contain poems'. That remark was certainly nearer the truth
than a subsequent one to John Davenport to the effect that
Church had cut out 'all the best stories'. But in saying on that
occasion that the stories selected 'are, mostly, very tame', he

was referring to the point which had been at issue all along: the question of taste involved in some of the tales.

Many of the short stories included here, with their strange imagination, emphasize ingredients organic also to the *Prospect* stories. The immediate connection is explained by the fact that Thomas for several years contemplated many of his stories as sections of a novel, 'the linking together of several short story sequences'. Writing to Pamela Hansford Johnson in May 1934 he informed her that

> My novel of the Jarvis valley is slower than ever. I have already scrapped two chapters of it. It is as ambitious as the Divine Comedy, with a chorus of deadly sins, anagrammatised as old gentlemen, with the incarnated figures of Love and Death, an Ulyssean page of thought from the minds of two anagrammatical spinsters, Miss P. and Miss R. Sion-Rees, an Immaculate Conception, a baldheaded girl, a celestial tramp, a mock Christ, and the Holy Ghost.

The 'chorus of deadly sins' are 'The Holy Six', and the 'Immaculate Conception' is also to be found in that story, just as the 'mock Christ' is the crucified idiot in 'The Tree'.

No doubt stories which relied for their effect on ingenuity of plot, or dealt with more ordinary experience, would have appeared tame and unattractive to the young writer at this time, for several reasons. But this alone would not account for the consistent relish with which he turns to his actual material. Neither does one feel that the stories were made strange and idiosyncratic merely to startle a possible reading audience: the 'Red Notebook', like the four poetry 'Notebooks', was initially very much a private record of an equally private imagination. Thomas's gift, whether he consciously realized it or not, was in the first place essentially a verbal and imaginative one. And it was for him, in his initial suburban obscurity, enough of a task to body forth that gift, without training, controlling or chastening it too rigorously. His early career is a classic record of a young writer eschewing, because of some curious urgency, formal disciplines like plot in prose and developing structure in poetry.

The primary impetus in that early career was the need for

self-revelation and self-realization. A record of this exists in the poet's early correspondence with his friend Trevor Hughes, who was sending Thomas some of his own prose. In Thomas's advice to Hughes at the time we find the implicit reflection of his own motives and methods. Basically, Thomas was concerned with 'sincerity'. He held that fidelity to the kind of material which comes to mind with the least conscious prompting was important ('the faster I write the more sincere I am in what I write'). In essence, his advice to Hughes was 'to delve deep, deep, into yourself until you find your soul, and until you know yourself'. Much of what he writes in this connection is an earlier version of his later statement about dragging hidden things into the naked light. The adolescent Thomas explored through fictive narratives as much as through his poems those human energies which adolescence feels so tangibly. In the correspondence with Hughes he clearly found a means of rationalizing his own position:

> This is my main contention: Why, when you can, as you show in your letters, struggle with the fundamentals of belief, and the rock-bottom ideas of artistic bewilderment, morbidity and disillusionment, when you can write with a pen dipped in fire and vinegar, when you have something to say, however terrible it may be, and the vocabulary to say it with, do you waste time on the machinations of a Stacy Aumonier plot and on the unreal emotions of a paste-board character whose replica one could find in a hundred novelettes of the 'nineties'? Why go to the cafés and French cafés at that, for your plots? You are not really interested in people. I doubt whether you are a fiction writer at all. Why go to the cafés for worn plots when the only things you are interested in are the antagonistic interplay of emotions and ideas, the rubbing together of sensibilities, brain chords and nerve chords, convolutions of style, tortuities of new expressions?

In the previous year (1932), he had described his own position to Hughes: 'I wish I loved the human race; but ghouls, vampires, women-rippers . . . pass by the window, going God knows where or why, in a dream up and down the hill.' All the material that his suburban, provincial context as an adolescent in Cwmdonkin Drive might have provided as human subject-matter is rejected in favour of a different kind of emotional material. Instead, he creates a semi-mythical world and exercises a view of life which disintegrates and demoralizes ('Everything we do drags up a devil').

It is a view of minor prose fiction as something essentially revelatory and therapeutic. He rejected the appearances of a working-day humanity, and the decision was for Thomas a release from the inevitable material which—with one exception, Caradoc Evans—had settled comfortably with its own kind of falsification into the Anglo-Welsh tradition. It is no accident that Thomas at this time was very much in favour of Evans's distorting view of the passions and prejudices of his people. But Thomas's prose did not have the same objective aims. The thing to be revealed was something concerned more with inner than with outer weather. Other notable writers were swept into his discussion:

> You know Middleton Murry's prose, and Lawrence's non-fiction prose. Murry is not interested in plots or characters. He is interested in the symbols of the world, in the fundamentals of the soul. And these things he writes about. These things *you* are interested in. Write about them . . . Write a story (if you must write stories) about yourself searching for your soul amid the horrors of corruption and disease, about your passionate strivings after something you don't know and can't express. (This is one of the few ways of knowing it and expressing it.)

The immediate purpose in emphasizing this hectic, therapeutic programme for his friend was to free him from the morbidity of temperament which Hughes's unfortunate encounters with family sickness and death had made habitual. For Thomas, no such realistic, first-hand encounters with human suffering had at this time come within his range of immediate experience: 'I can't appreciate it, firstly because I have known very little physical suffering and no actual hardships or heart-breaks, and secondly because, at the root of it all, I can't reconcile life and art.'

A statement of that kind could stand usefully as the apology for the essentially extra-social nature of Thomas's early

material, in his poetry as well as in his prose. Experienced pain
and disappointment, realistically dealt with, could only enter
the poet's prose in 1939 when, for example, he wrote a moving
and subtle account of a truant schoolboy journey he made with
Hughes out to the Worm's Head ('Who Do You Wish Was
With Us?' in the *Portrait*). But frustration experienced in the
outer, social world (the 'life' he couldn't reconcile with art) was
not the only spur which could prompt a programme such as he
urged on Hughes. Its equivalent in Thomas was the matrix of
adolescent fears and intimations which fired prose and poetry
alike. This is what he found 'real'—material 'sincere' enough,
therefore, for exploration ('my book is going to be as nice as me').

Such prose, then, is mainly self-revelatory—the prose of
sensibility. Its imagination, its Romantic Agony, is paralleled
in poems like 'When like a running grave' and 'It is the sinners
dust-tongued bell'. There is a response here to the ambiguous
nature of life. The embarrassed juxtaposition of Christian and
pagan elements gives a picture of nature unsure of herself. The
dark frustration of a mind unsure of a rational, ordained
universe, the strong awareness of emblematic death and decay,
causes Thomas to body forth and celebrate a strong anti-life
imagination. Exaggerated emphasis is placed on the physicality
of existence in a sexually-driven world. The writer celebrates
that side of life which the conscious mind is most afraid of—the
irrational and elemental, the negative forces. Thus, where there
is a received symbol of life and regeneration, it is modulated
into perverse negative forms, as in the birth of Christ in a war-
torn town in 'Gaspar, Melchior, Balthasar' (compare the
mock-crucifixion in 'The Tree'). Where there is a basic
realistic situation at the heart of the story, the only drama it can
be given is the shattering of ordinariness by violence, as with the
pathetic girl imprisoned by domesticity in 'The True Story'
(compare the girl in the poem 'Paper and Sticks') or the grey
victim of 'The Vest'. 'The Holy Six' lets loose, and makes
concretely active, anti-life forces anagrammatized as Rafe
(fear), Lucytre (cruelty), Stul (lust) and so on. The self-image
reflected in the lover's eye, as it might appear in a poem by
Donne, gets outrageous employment in 'The Burning Baby':
Rhys Rhys 'had not felt love like this since the woman who
scratched him, seeing the woman witch in his male eyes, had

fallen into his arms.' What the 'sowfaced woman Llareggub'
had taught Rhys Rhys's idiot son were 'the terrors of the flesh'.
No wonder, then, that another 'novel' (of which 'Prologue to
an Adventure' was to form a part) was to be a 'reversed
version of *Pilgrim's Progress*': 'It's based on the *Pilgrim's
Progress*, but tells of the adventures of anti-Christian in his
travels from the city of Zion to the City of Destruction.' Thomas,
like other writers of the literature of sensibility as described in
Northrop Frye's words, is 'attracted by the ruinous and the
mephitic, or by the primeval and "unspoiled".' The latter
tendency—the surrender to an Adamic vision—came into its
own only in the second half of Thomas's career, in the poetry of
remembered childhood, and the later prose.

Nothing could stress more forcefully the essential difference
between the writer's imagination in the earlier and in the later
phase of his career than the way in which minor details from the
early tales are resurrected in the comic, optimistic idiom of the
later prose. One might compare the pelts and bones which
litter the idiot's room in 'The Burning Baby' with the trophies
on the poet's wall in the *Portrait*. Or consider the detail which
marks the weird idiosyncrasy of the Rev. Rhys Rhys himself—
'the stem of his pipe stuck between his flybuttons, the bible
unopened upon his knees'. Nothing could be further from the
endearing detail of the Reverend Eli Jenkins later in *Under Milk
Wood*, dipping his pen in his cocoa! Llareggub, as it is mentioned (for the first time, in fact) in 'The Burning Baby' is a
different concept from 'the place of love'. And yet, in 'The
Horse's Ha' the descriptive technique of the Play for Voices is
already being exercised: 'Out came the grocer with an egg in
his hand, and the butcher in a bloody coat'; 'out came the
undertaker in a frock coat; distrusting the light of the moon, he
carried a candle in his gloved hand, the candle casting three
shadows'; 'Butcher and baker fell asleep that night, their
women sleeping at their sides'; 'Cathmarw, in a bath of blood,
slept still for the light day'. What we see is a progression
towards comedy. The context and purpose, therefore, differ as
we move from 'The Holy Six'—

> God's wrath, cried Mr Rafe, in the shadow of a voice, nothing
> that was not half the substance of a man writhing in his

shadow as it fell aslant on the hill, on the double-thumbed
piksies about me. Down, down—he slashed at the blades—
down, you bald girls from Merthyr

to the *Portrait*—

Mr. Mathews cast down the scarlet town, drove out the bare-
bellied boys who danced around the ice-cream man, and
wound the girls' sunburnt thighs about with his black overcoat—'Down! down!' he cried, 'the night is upon us'

to *Under Milk Wood*—

Jack Black sleeps in a nightshirt tied to his ankles with elastic
and dreams of
                              SECOND VOICE

   chasing the naughty couples down the grassgreen goose-
berried double bed of the wood, flogging the tosspots in the
spit-and-sawdust, driving out the bare bold girls from the
sixpenny hops of his nightmares.

                    JACK BLACK (*Loudly*)
                         Ach y fi!
                         Ach y fi!

From imaginative nightmare, the prose gradually emerged into
the light of common day in the *Portrait* and went on to the comic
optimism of the Play for Voices.

PART I

BREMBER

From *Swansea Grammar School Magazine*, vol. 28, no. 1 (April 1931), pp. 139–40.

From the stairs, the shadows slid gently down into the hall. He could see the dark outline of the banisters reflected across the mirror, and the arc of the chandelier throwing its light. But that was all. Towards the door, the shadows became larger. Then they were lost in the darkness of the floor and ceiling. He fumbled in his pocket for a match, and lit the taper in his hand. Holding the tiny flame above his head, he turned the handle and stepped into the room. There was a smell of dust and old wood. It was curious how sensitive he was to it, how it quickened his imagination. Old ladies making lace by the light of the moon, their thin, pale fingers stealing along the brocade, their ageless cheeks tinted like a little child's. That was what the room always reminded him of, since the days when he had first tiptoed in, and gazed with terror at the windows opening on to the grey lawn, and the trees beyond. Or when, still a little boy, he had sat at the harpsichord, touching the dusty keys so lightly no one could hear their sound, afraid, and yet entranced as the music rose faintly into the air. It was always sad. He could detect the desolate sadness beneath the lightest fugue; as his hand touched the notes, there were tears in his eyes, a great longing for something he had known and had forgotten, loved but had lost.

That was a number of years ago, and now the same sensation of unreality and of longing came over him as he lit the harpsichord's long candles with his taper, and saw in their spreading light, the walls crowd closer round him, and the heavy chairs hem him in. The keys were as dusty as ever. He brushed them lightly with his sleeve, then let his fingers wander for a moment over them. How frail their sound was. What curious little melodies they made, so sad and yet so perfect. For a moment he thought he heard the sound of childish footsteps outside the door, running down the corridor into the darkness. But then they were gone, and he could but suppose that they had never been. Now there was a hint of laughter sounding in his ears; now it was gone again. As he played, he seemed to hear the soft, rustling noise of a silk skirt dragged along the ground. Then his music grew louder, and, when it was soft again, there was nothing.

Try as he would, he could not analyse his reasons for coming to the house. It terrified him, and yet he could not draw away from it. Out on the road he had suddenly felt the desire to throw apart the veil of the years, to bring back to him all that old house had meant, the dusk, the soft voices in the corridors, the harpsichord, the stairs that wound interminably up into the dark, the thousand details of the rooms, the soft, insinuating fear that looked out of corners, and never went away. He had walked up the drive to the front door. The lion's head on the door-knocker grinned down at him. He lifted it, and struck the wood. No one answered. Again and again he knocked, but the house was quiet. He put his shoulder to the door. It swung open. He had tip-toed along the passages, looked into the rooms, touched the familiar objects. Nothing had changed. And then, when the night had crept out of the leaded windows, he had closed the door of the music-room softly behind him. He was filled with a great relief. The longing always at the back of his mind was realized, the lost thing found, and the forgotten thing remembered. This was the end of the journey.

Momentarily, the candles became brighter. He was able to see further into the room. Rising, he walked across, and picked up a dusty book laid on the table. 'The House of Brember.' He brought it over to the light. Each page was familiar to him, the family, generation by generation, men of thought rather than of action, all visionaries who saw the world from the cloud of their own dreaming. He turned over the pages, until he came to the last: George Henry Brember, last of the line, died. . . .

He looked down on his name, and then closed the book.

JARLEY'S

From *Swansea Grammar School Magazine*, vol. 30, no. 3 (December 1933), pp. 137–9. Signed 'Old Boy', and attributed to Thomas by the Swansea Public Library on the authority of George H. Gwynne, a former master at the school. Thomas had left the school in July 1931.

On the day that the travelling waxworks came to town the attendant vanished. Next morning the proprietor called at the employment agency and asked for a smart lad who could talk English. But the smart lads talked Welsh, and the boy from Bristol had a harelip. So the proprietor returned to his lodgings and, passing the canal, saw Eleazar reading on the bank.

'Any luck?' he enquired.

'I'm not fishing,' replied Eleazar.

He was immediately engaged.

*   *   *

It was late in the evening, and the last curious visitor had left the tent. The proprietor counted the day's takings and went away leaving Eleazar alone in the dark, wax world. Eleazar removed the last cigarette-end from the ground, and brought out a duster from his pocket. Tremblingly he dusted over the lean, brown body of Hiawatha; tremblingly he patted the pale cheeks of Charlie Peace; tremblingly he dusted over the wax neck of Circe.

'You forgot my left calf,' said Hiawatha.

'You forgot my top lip,' said Charlie Peace.

'You forgot my right shoulder,' said the temptress.

Eleazar looked at the wax figures in amazement.

'You heard me,' said Hiawatha.

'You heard me,' said Charlie Peace.

'You heard me,' said the temptress.

5

Eleazar stared around him. The entrance to the tent was a long way off. There was no escape.

'Calf,' said Hiawatha.

'Lip,' said Charlie Peace.

'Shoulder,' said Circe.

Tremblingly Eleazar dusted over the strong-muscled calf; tremblingly he patted the snarling lip; tremblingly he dusted over the wax shoulder.

'That is certainly better,' said Hiawatha. 'You see,' he continued in apology, 'I used to run a lot; and you want your calves dusted then, don't you?'

'I do a lot of snarling,' said Charlie Peace.

'I do a lot of tempting,' said the temptress; 'though, really, I should be losing my fascination by this time; and my shoulder is not all that it was. I had it bitten in Aberdare once.'

'I remember the night well,' said Hiawatha. 'Somebody put an old hat on me.'

'I remember the night,' remarked the murderer, 'when as a child I stuck a needle into my nurse: it was a darning needle.'

'I remember chasing Minnehaha all over the rapids,' said Hiawatha. 'She used to be terribly annoyed when I called her Laughing Water.'

'I remember the sea-green eyes of Jason,' said Circe.

Eleazar could remember nothing. His first fears had vanished to be replaced by a sense of friendly curiosity. He inquired politely if all was well in the state of wax.

'Indeed,' said Hiawatha, 'I have little to complain of. There is a great deal to be said for being wax. One has few troubles. It is difficult to receive injury. The sharpest arrow could do little to me: a momentary impression soon to be filled in with a farthing's worth of wax from the local stores. It is a perpetual source of wonder to me that more people do not realise the advantages of a wax life.'

'How is it with you, ma'am?' asked Eleazar.

'There is still the desire to tempt,' replied the temptress, 'that I cannot conquer. And I still remember those confounded sea-green eyes.'

'Murder as a profession,' began Charlie Peace . . .

'Henry Wadsworth,' began Hiawatha . . .

'The history of temptation,' began the temptress . . .

And suddenly the three wax figures were still.

Eleazar shuffled further along the tent.

'Eleazar,' said an ape.

'Sir?' said Eleazar.

'Life,' said the ape, 'is a never-ending mystery. We are born. Why are we born? We die. The reason is obvious. The life of the body is short, and the veins are incapable of holding an eternal supply of blood.'

Eleazar would have continued on his way, but the ape held up its hand. 'Stop,' said the ape. 'Consider the man of flesh and the man of wax. Everything is done for the wax man; he is made painlessly and skilfully; he is found a house in a nice waterproof tent or in the interior of a large and hygienic building; he is clothed, brushed and dusted; he is the cynosure of all eyes. Think of the opportunities he enjoys to study the mentality of his near neighbour-man. Day after day, the faces of men are pressed close to mine; I see into men's eyes; I listen to their conversations. The man of wax is an unchanging, unprejudiced and unemotional observer of the human comedy.'

'Sir,' said Eleazar, 'you talk very well for an ape.'

'Eleazar,' said the ape, 'I have known this frame of wax for two days only. I was the late attendant.'

'Tell me,' said Eleazar, 'do you feel the cold?'

'Neither cold nor warmth.'

'Do you feel hunger?'

'Neither hunger nor thirst. I feel nothing. I want nothing. I am perpetually happy.'

Eleazar removed his jacket and trousers.

'Make room—move up,' said Eleazar.

*   *   *

Next morning the proprietor called at the employment agency, and asked for a smart lad.

'He must be careful, too,' he explained, 'for my waxworks has just been presented with an expensive new figure.'

'An historical figure?'

'No, no,' said the proprietor; 'the figure of a Welsh Druid in a long white shirt.'

THE TRUE STORY

From *Yellowjacket*, vol. 1, no. 2 (May 1939), pp. 60–3. Entered in 'The Red Notebook' (now in the Lockwood Memorial Library, Buffalo, N.Y.) as 'Martha' (pp. 10–13v.) and dated 22 January 1934. For publication, the girl's name was changed to Helen. 'The Red Notebook' is numbered (recto only) 2–53, and contains the following stories in early manuscript form: 'The Tree', 'Martha', 'After the Fair', 'The Enemies', 'The Dress', 'The Visitors' [*sic*], 'The Vest', 'Gaspar, Melchior, Balthasar', 'The Burning Baby' and 'Mr. Tritas On The Roofs' (or 'Anagram'), the last being an early version of 'The Orchards'. The notebook covers the period 28 December 1933 to October 1934.

The old woman upstairs had been dying since Helen could remember. She had lain like a wax woman in her sheets since Helen was a child coming with her mother to bring fresh fruit and vegetables to the dying. And now Helen was a woman under her apron and print frock and her pale hair was bound in a bunch behind her head. Each morning she got up with the sun, lit the fire, let in the red-eyed cat. She made a pot of tea and, going up to the bedroom at the back of the cottage, bent over the old woman whose unseeing eyes were never closed. Each morning she looked into the hollows of the eyes and passed her hands over them. But the lids did not move, and she could not tell if the old woman breathed. 'Eight o'clock, eight o'clock now,' she said. And at once the eyes smiled. A ragged hand came out from the sheets and stayed there until Helen took it in her padded hand and closed it round the cup. When the cup was empty Helen filled it, and when the pot was dry she pulled back the white sheets from the bed. There the old woman was, stretched out in her nightdress, and the colour of her flesh was grey as her hair. Helen tidied the sheets and attended to the old woman's wants. Then she took the pot away.

Each morning she made breakfast for the boy who worked in

8

the garden. She went to the back door, opened it, and saw him in the distance with his spade. 'Half past eight now,' she said. He was an ugly boy and his eyes were redder than the cat's, two crafty cuts in his head forever spying on the first shadows of her breast. She put his food in front of him. When he stood up he always said, 'Is there anything you want me to do?' She had never said, 'Yes.' The boy went back to dig potatoes out of the patch or to count the hens' eggs, and if there were berries to be picked off the garden bushes she joined him before noon. Seeing the red currants pile up in the palm of her hand, she would think of the stain of the money under the old woman's mattress. If there were hens to be killed she could cut their throats far more cleanly than the boy who let his knife stay in the wound and wiped the blood on the knife along his sleeve. She caught a hen and killed it, felt its warm blood, and saw it run headless up the path. Then she went in to wash her hands.

It was in the first weeks of spring that she made up her mind to kill the old woman upstairs. She was twenty years old. There was so much that she wanted. She wanted a man of her own and a black dress for Sundays and a hat with a flower. She had no money at all. On the days that the boy took the eggs and the vegetables to market she gave him sixpence that the old woman gave her, and the money the boy brought back in his handker-chief she put into the old woman's hand. She worked for her food and shelter as the boy worked for his, though she slept in a room upstairs and he slept in a straw bed over the empty sheds.

On a market morning she walked into the garden so that the plan might be cooled in her head. It was a fine May day with no more than two clouds in the sky, two unshapely hands closing round the head of the sun. 'If I could fly,' she thought, 'I could fly in at the open window and fix my teeth in her throat.' But the cool wind blew the thought away. She knew that she was no common girl, for she had read books in the winter evenings when the boy was dreaming in the straw and the old woman was alone in the dark. She had read of a god who came down like money, of snakes with the voices of men, and of a man who stood on the top of a hill talking with a piece of fire.

At the end of the garden where the fence kept out the wild,

green fields she came to a mound of earth. There she had
buried the dog she had killed for catching and killing the hens.
On a rough cross the date of the death was written backwards
so that the dog had not died yet. 'I could bury her here,' said
Helen to herself, 'By the side of the grave, so that nobody could
find her.' And she patted her hands and reached the back door
of the cottage before the two clouds got round the sun.

Inside there was a meal to be prepared for the old woman,
potatoes to be mashed up in the tea. With the knife in her hand
and the skins in her lap, she thought of the murder she was
about to do. The knife made the only sound, the wind had
dropped down, her heart was as quiet as though she had
wrapped it up. Nothing moved in the cottage; her hand was
dead on her lap; she could not think that smoke went up the
chimney and out into the still sky. Her mind, alone in the world,
was ticking away. Then, when all things were dead, a cock
crew, and she remembered the boy who would soon be back
from market. She had made up her mind to kill before he
returned, but the grave must be dug and the hole filled up.
Helen felt her hand die again in her lap. And in the middle of
death she heard the boy's hand lift the latch. He came into the
kitchen, saw that she was cleaning the potatoes, and dropped
his handkerchief on the table. Hearing the rattle of money, she
looked up at him and smiled. He had never seen her smile
before.

Soon she put his meal in front of him, and sat sideways by the
fire. As he raised the knife to his mouth, he felt the full glance of
her eyes on the sides of his eyes. 'Have you taken up her
dinner?' he asked. She did not answer. When he had finished
he stood up from the table and asked, 'Is there anything you
want me to do?' as he had asked a thousand times. 'Yes,' said
Helen.

She had never said 'Yes' to him before. He had never heard
a woman speak as she did then. The first shadow of her breast
had never been so dark. He stumbled across the kitchen to her
and she lifted her hands to her shoulders. 'What will you do for
me?' she said, and loosened the straps of her frock so that it fell
about her and left her breast bare. She took his hand and
placed it on her flesh. He stared at her nakedness, then said her
name and caught hold of her. She held him close. 'What will

you do for me?' She let her frock fall on the floor and tore the rest of her clothes away. 'You will do what I want,' she said as his hands dropped on her.

After a minute she struggled out of his arms and ran softly across the room. With her naked back to the door that led upstairs, she beckoned him and told him what he was to do. 'You help me, we shall be rich,' she said. He smiled and nodded. He tried to finger her again but she caught his fingers and opened the door and led him upstairs. 'You stay here quiet,' she said. In the old woman's room she looked around her as if for the last time, at the cracked jug, the half-open window, the bed and the text on the wall. 'One o'clock now,' she said into the old woman's ear, and the blind eyes smiled. Helen put her fingers round the old woman's throat. 'One o'clock now,' she said, and with a sudden movement knocked the old woman's head against the wall. It needed but three little knocks, and the head burst like an egg.

'What have you done?' cried the boy. Helen called for him to come in. He stared at the naked woman who cleaned her hands on the bed and at the blood that made a round, red stain on the wall, and screamed out in horror. 'Be quiet,' said Helen, but he screamed again at her quiet voice and scurried downstairs.

'So Helen must fly,' she said to herself. 'Fly out of the old woman's room.' She opened the window wider and stepped out. 'I am flying,' she said.

But she was not flying.

THE VEST

From *Yellowjacket*, vol. 1, no. 2 (May 1939), pp. 64–7. Entered in 'The Red Notebook' (pp. 33–8), dated 20 July 1934, where the girl was called Helen.

He rang the bell. There was no answer. She was out. He turned the key.

The hall in the late afternoon light was full of shadows. They made one almost solid shape. He took off his hat and coat, looking sideways, so that he might not see the shape, at the light through the sitting-room door.

'Is anybody in?'

The shadows bewildered him. She would have swept them up as she swept the invading dust.

In the drawing-room the fire was low. He crossed over to it and sat down. His hands were cold. He needed the flames of the fire to light up the corners of the room. On the way home he had seen a dog run over by a motorcar. The sight of the blood had confused him. He had wanted to go down on his knees and finger the blood that made a round pool in the middle of the road. Someone had plucked at his sleeve, asking him if he was ill. He remembered that the sound and strength of his voice had drowned the first desire. He had walked away from the blood, with the stained wheels of the car and the soaking blackness under the bonnet going round and round before his eyes. He needed the warmth. The wind outside had cut between his fingers and thumbs.

She had left her sewing on the carpet near the coal-scuttle. She had been making a petticoat. He picked it up and touched it, feeling where her breasts would sit under the yellow cotton. That morning he had seen her with her head enveloped in a frock. He saw her, thin in her nakedness, as a bag of skin and henna drifting out of the light. He let the petticoat drop on to the floor again.

Why, he wondered, was there this image of the red and broken dog? It was the first time he had seen the brains of a living creature burst out of the skull. He had been sick at the last yelp and the sudden caving of the dog's chest. He could have killed and shouted, like a child cracking a blackbeetle between its fingers.

A thousand nights ago, she had lain by his side. In her arms, he thought of the bones of her arms. He lay quietly by her skeleton. But she rose next morning in the corrupted flesh.

When he hurt her, it was to hide his pain. When he struck her cheek until the skin blushed, it was to break the agony of his own head. She told him of her mother's death. Her mother had worn a mask to hide the illness at her face. He felt the locust of that illness on his own face, in the mouth and the fluttering eyelid.

The room was darkening. He was too tired to shovel the fire into life, and saw the last flame die. A new coldness blew in with the early night. He tasted the sickness of the death of the flame as it rose to the tip of his tongue, and swallowed it down. It ran around the pulse of the heart, and beat until it was the only sound. And all the pain of the damned. The pain of a man with a bottle breaking across his face, the pain of a cow with a calf dancing out of her, the pain of the dog, moved through him from his aching hair to the flogged soles of his feet.

His strength returned. He and the dripping calf, the man with the torn face, and the dog on giddy legs, rose up as one, in one red brain and body, challenging the beast in the air. He heard the challenge in his snapping thumb and finger, as she came in.

He saw that she was wearing her yellow hat and frock.

'Why are you sitting in the dark?' she said.

She went into the kitchen to light the stove. He stood up from his chair. Holding his hands out in front of him as though they were blind, he followed her. She had a box of matches in her hand. As she took out a dead match and rubbed it on the box, he closed the door behind him. 'Take off your frock,' he said.

She did not hear him, and smiled.

'Take off your frock,' he said.

She stopped smiling, took out a live match and lit it.

'Take off your frock,' he said.

He stepped towards her, his hands still blind. She bent over the stove. He blew the match out.

'What is it?' she said.

His lips moved, but he did not speak.

'Why?' she said.

He slapped her cheek quite lightly with his open hand.

'Take off your frock,' he said.

He heard her frock rustle over her head, and her frightened sob as he touched her. Methodically his blind hands made her naked.

He walked out of the kitchen, and closed the door.

In the hall, the one married shadow had broken up. He could not see his own face in the mirror as he tied his scarf and stroked the brim of his hat. There were too many faces. Each had a section of his features, and each a stiffened lock of his hair. He pulled up the collar of his coat. It was a wet winter night. As he walked, he counted the lamps. He pushed a door open and stepped into the warmth. The room was empty. The woman behind the bar smiled as she rubbed two coins together. 'It's a cold night,' she said.

He drank up the whisky and went out.

He walked on through the increasing rain. He counted the lamps again, but they reached no number.

The corner bar was empty. He took his drink into the saloon, but the saloon was empty.

The Rising Sun was empty.

Outside, he heard no traffic. He remembered that he had seen nobody in the streets. He cried aloud in a panic of loneliness:

'Where are you, where are you?'

Then there was traffic, and the windows were blazing. He heard singing from the house on the corner.

The bar was crowded. Women were laughing and shouting. They spilt their drinks over their dresses and lifted their dresses up. Girls were dancing on the sawdust. A woman caught him by the arm, and rubbed his face on her sleeve, and took his hand in hers and put it on her throat. He could hear nothing but the voices of the laughing women and the shouting of the girls as they danced. Then the ungainly women from the seats and the corners rocked towards him. He saw that the room was full of women. Slowly, still laughing, they gathered close to him.

He whispered a word under his breath, and felt the old sickness turn sour in his belly. There was blood before his eyes.

Then he, too, burst into laughter. He stuck his hands deep in the pockets of his coat, and laughed into their faces.

His hand clutched around a softness in his pocket. He drew out his hand, the softness in it.

The laughter died. The room was still. Quiet and still, the women stood watching him.

He raised his hand up level with his eyes. It held a piece of soft cloth.

'Who'll buy a lady's vest,' he said, 'Going, going, ladies, who'll buy a lady's vest.'

The meek and ordinary women in the bar stood still, their glasses in their hands, as he leant with his back to the counter and shouted with laughter and waved the bloody cloth in front of them.

IN THE GARDEN

From *Swansea Grammar School Magazine*, vol. 31, no. 2 (July 1934), pp. 69–70, signed O.B. [Old Boy]. The editor agrees with R. N. Maud that, on internal evidence, this story is attributable to Dylan Thomas; see Maud, 'Dylan Thomas in Welsh Periodicals', *The National Library of Wales Journal*, vol. 15, no. 3 (1968), p. 287, footnote.

The boy was more afraid of the dark garden than of anything else in the world. It was frightening enough in the twilight, but when there was blackness above and below and the trees spoke among themselves, the garden was too terrible to think about.

He tried to convince himself that behind the red curtains there lay nothing at all, and that there was nothing at all anywhere, only the bright room, his mother, and himself. In the morning, the garden was full of delight; the grass was long and unkempt; there were sunflowers that nobody had planted there. Against the further wall was a summerhouse, the home of beetles, where he kept his collection of strange pebbles and his picture-postcards. There he would sit for as long as the sunlight lasted, with his back against the wood box on the seat, and his feet on an old and mysterious trunk. The trunk was all the more fascinating because there was nothing in it at all. Once he had prised up the rusty padlock with his pocket knife and very fearfully opened the lid, to find only emptiness and the smell of rot. He felt sure that it must have a secret drawer somewhere that held precious stones as bright as the sun, and he planned, when he should discover them, to sell the treasure to a rich merchant, in return for a journey to the parrot-haunted islands.

But as the last rags of the sunset withered away behind the tallest chimney stack, he would hear the warning voices telling him that it was time for him to go, and he knew that somewhere in the approaching shadows were the ugly night-tenants of the garden. Then he would close the door of the summer house very slowly and carefully, and walk up the garden path until he reached the three stone steps that led down to the scullery. These he would take at one leap, and run quickly into the house with all the devils of darkness at his heels.

It was a very hot night. The windows were open, and the spinning jinnies whirled into the house to shake their long legs in the glare of the gas. The boy liked to watch them for as long as they kept to the ceiling, but he hated them when they fell dizzily on to the table cloth or flew blindly into his face, and worst of all he hated the great grey moths that blundered round the room, for he knew they were in league with the things in the garden outside.

'It's hot in here,' his mother said suddenly, 'put out the chairs on the lawn.'

She left him alone in the kitchen. He picked up a chair, then set it down again and went out into the scullery. He opened the garden door, and a great moth flew into his face. Then he stepped out into the garden and faced the enemies.

Hooded and gloved in black, they lined the paths and stood across the grass. He squared his shoulders and mounted bravely to the top of the steps. He could not see the faces of the shadows, but they could see his face, for he was framed in the light from the open door. He thought of the summerhouse in the morning, friendly, dusted with light, and of the trunk where the treasure lay. He went out on to the edge of the grass, and he could not hear the warning of the trees for the drumming of his heart. As he advanced, the shadows curtsied and fell back a little, leaving his path clear to the darkness that was most dreadful of all.

Then he stopped, for he was more afraid than he thought he could ever be. The garden writhed about him, and the walls and the trees shot upward so that he could not see the sky. The pointed roof of the summerhouse shot up the dark like a steeple hat. The boy dared not look behind him, for he knew that he was surrounded by his foes, and that their arms were linked behind his back. Very, very soon, they would close in upon him, as though they were playing an innocent game of Poor Jenny Lies A-Weeping, and one of them would throw a hood over his head. He waited and waited and still nothing happened, only the gradual mounting of the trees, the walls, and the wrongly shaped tower to the sky. He could not see them, for now his hands were over his eyes. The ring closed in upon him. He could hear their feet in the ragged grass and the slipping of their robes over the damp soil.

He threw back his head and stared straight into the eyes of the tallest shadow. For a long while he stared. Then he smiled at his friend the shadow, and held out his arms. The door of the summerhouse swung back in the wind, and he saw that the trunk, lying open on its side, was full of fire. The precious stones poured from it in streams of silver, of gold and of blue. The garden was bright with their colour.

He opened his arms a little wider, and the stones leapt upward to his breast. He smiled at the silent watchers and they dared not meet his eyes. Slowly they melted away, and the trees melted with them. He gathered up the jewels, and, slipping on to his knees, he laid them in the lap of his friend. The door of the summerhouse closed softly with the falling of the latch, the wind dropped, and still the boy smiled and did not move.

His mother called to him. She called to him again, and still he did not answer, so she ran into the garden with his name on her lips. There, in the middle of the grass, she found the boy kneeling, his face in his hands, in the blinding light of the moon.

GASPAR, MELCHIOR, BALTHASAR

From the MS 'Red Notebook' (pp. 38v–40v), in the Lockwood Memorial Library, New York. The story is dated 8 August 1934. In this transcription, square brackets denote deletions and italics indicate superior additions by Dylan Thomas.

A flying fleet came out of the shadow, [the hangar of shadows,] and the arsenal of the iron mist, hovered over the island and, hidden in the smoke of the exhausts, dropped death upon the cities. The men in the cities raced for shelter, fixing their leather masks [upon their masks of flesh], their trousers un-buttoned as they scampered out of the urinals, their hair uncombed as they climbed out of a purchased sleep, [their typists unfingered as they] puffed out of tenement offices, cupping their hands for the exploding manna. Two lovers, struck by the same shell, fell into bliss. Down thumped a ripper of women, a [lady] *woman* with rings on her fingers in the [common blood, a starver of babies, a thief of money, a thief of leisure, and a thief of love in the] levelling gutter. Bullets broke up the hungry ranks. Crow food sliced about them [and the flesh of their slave-masters raw in the streets, they starved in the heart of plenty, starved for the food of the heart the galvanic wheat that death beat back into the bone. Death flew over the island cities, and then flew back into the hangar of the shadow of death.]

The workers in the south and the north of the island, where death had fallen thinly, were provided with guns and shafts of steel [and little pinned grenades]. They cocked the guns and laughed up at the shadow above them [, pointing the barrels at the high men of the island. They slew the givers of arms. They looted the shops, and raped the widows, and burgled the hearts of the dead, finding the keys of hate in the opened pulses. There was love and hate in the island, out of the spirits of death a new, reeking life, out of the last hacked coals a new fire]. Street rose against street, and city against city. In the ruined cities, along the deserted streets where the dead on the pavements fell apart, the dying spoke women's names, [and the vermin from the blown sewers gnawed at their chests,] the shadow moved. I saw two ghosts in the avenue by the broken park. They moved among the dead, prying into each shot face, [upon] [on] each [empty] hollow head, and under each folded eye.

The ships were unloaded at the wharves, the engines cold in the stations, the printing presses silent, and the sentries before the island palace stiff [, split like cabbages,] in their boxes. In the parks the birds were singing, a new froth was on the trees, the wind blew the waste paper up the paths. [I remember] I walked all that morning, a ghost [in a springing world, a solid man in a world that was all a ghost]. Wherever I walked, in street or under arch, on the grass of the green parks, through alley and slum down to the edge of the corpsy water, I saw the two ghosts searching. They moved among the dead, questioning each dead eye, invisibly touching the hems of the dresses, the young, triangular breasts, *the* soft heart, [and] *the* hard loins.

The guns grew quieter in the distance. The last of the first revolution died away in a splutter of fire from the east of the great city. [I pattered, silent in my leather like a living man locked and forgotten in a mortuary,] I walked in strange thoroughfares and through the unlit centre of the city, strange itself in its first blindness. As I journeyed through the first stages of the night, coming upon the two ghosts now at a dark corner, now in the shadow of a doorway, and bent forever over the riddled dead, I held my scarf to my face for the smell of the dead flowering Black plague would branch from these blacker plants that shot to heaven through the wounds of the unburied fallen. I made my image as I walked, and the hemlock and the upas sprouted for me from the gutter beds.

It was a minute before midnight that I saw a lantern swinging at the end of a street. It was [a red rose] *bright and sweet* among the flowers that stank at my side, but, as I moved towards it, I felt the wind of the two ghosts as they drifted past me, and I followed them, calling them by name. There were men at the corner, dark-eyed behind their lantern.

'Who goes there?' they [said] cried.

They swung the lantern before my face.

'*Let me pass*', *I said*.

[Who are you, comrade?] they [said] cried again.

Where are you going?

[Let me pass]

[Who are you, comrade? they said]

[Of the wise men, I cried, let me pass]

[Where are you going, comrade?]

[Fools, fools, I cried, and] I waited no longer *but* knocked the lantern from their hands and plunged into the darkness after the windy ghosts. *I ran on and on, with* the noise of the revolvers behind me, [I ran on and on,] through a maze of alleys into a moonlit square.

There stood the two ghosts. At their feet lay a dead woman, naked but for her shawl, with a bayonet wound in her breasts. Slowly I stepped towards her. [Her time had been well upon her when they cut her down.] [But] As I watched, [the] *a* miraculous life stirred in her belly, and the arms of the child in [the] *her* womb [of the dead mother] broke, lifted, through the flesh.

The two ghosts bowed down.

Gold, said [Gaspar] *the first ghost*, [holding] *raising* a *golden* shadow to the light of the moon.

Frankincense, said [Melchior] *the second ghost* and his shadowy gift smoked from him.

The noise of the guns grew nearer and still nearer.

[Kneeling] *I knelt* where I stood [I] *and* felt the new joy of pain as a bullet drove into my [lung] *breast*. I fell upon the pavement near the two lifted arms, and [, bitter as myrrh,] my [bitter] blood streamed *bitterly* on to the [mother's feet] emerging head.

THE BURNING BABY

From *Contemporary Poetry and Prose*, No. 1 (May 1936), pp. 10–14. Entered in 'The Red Notebook' (pp. 41–7), dated September 1934. The story is an imaginative treatment of fact. Dr William Price of Llantrisant (1800–93)—Thomas's Rhys Rhys—christened an illegitimate son Iesu Grist (Jesus Christ). After the child's death, Price, who thought himself a Druid, burned his body on a hill in Caerlan fields, thus effecting what is accepted as being the earliest modern cremation in Britain. I am grateful to Mr Glyn Jones for information concerning the genesis of Thomas's story: he had related the above details to Thomas in an hotel room in Aberystwyth, where he had brought the poet to meet Caradoc Evans in September 1934.

They said that Rhys was burning his baby when a gorse bush broke into fire on the summit of the hill. The bush, burning merrily, assumed to them the sad white features and the rickety limbs of the vicar's burning baby. What the wind had not blown away of the baby's ashes, Rhys Rhys had sealed in a stone jar. With his own dust lay the baby's dust, and near him the dust of his daughter in a coffin of white wood.

They heard his son howl in the wind. They saw him walking over the hill, holding a dead animal up to the light of the stars. They saw him in the valley shadows as he moved, with the motion of a man cutting wheat, over the brows of the fields. In a sanatorium he coughed his lung into a basin, stirring his fingers delightedly in the blood. What moved with invisible scythe through the valley was a shadow and a handful of shadows cast by the grave sun.

The bush burned out, and the face of the baby fell away with the smoking leaves.

It was, they said, on a fine sabbath morning in the middle of the summer that Rhys Rhys fell in love with his daughter. The gorse that morning had burst into flames. Rhys Rhys, in clerical black, had seen the flames shoot up to the sky, and the

bush on the edge of the hill burn red as God among the paler
burning of the grass. He took his daughter's hand as she lay in
the garden hammock, and told her that he loved her. He told
her that she was more beautiful than her dead mother. Her hair
smelt of mice, her teeth came over her lip, and the lids of her
eyes were red and wet. He saw her beauty come out of her like a
stream of sap. The folds of her dress could not hide from him the
shabby nakedness of her body. It was not her bone, nor her
flesh, nor her hair that he found suddenly beautiful. The poor
soil shudders under the sun, he said. He moved his hand up and
down her arm. Only the awkward and the ugly, only the barren
bring forth fruit. The flesh of her arm was red with the smoothing of his hand. He touched her breast. From the touch of her
breast he knew each inch of flesh upon her. Why do you touch
me there? she said.

In the church that morning he spoke of the beauty of the
harvest, of the promise of the standing corn and the promise in
the sharp edge of the scythe as it brings the corn low and
whistles through the air before it cuts into the ripeness. Through
the open windows at the end of the aisles, he saw the yellow
fields upon the hillside and the smudge of heather on the
meadow borders. The world was ripe.

The world is ripe for the second coming of the son of man, he
said aloud.

But it was not the ripeness of God that glistened from the hill.
It was the promise and the ripeness of the flesh, the good flesh,
the mean flesh, flesh of his daughter, flesh, flesh, the flesh of the
voice of thunder howling before the death of man.

That night he preached of the sins of the flesh. O God in the
image of our flesh, he prayed.

His daughter sat in the front pew, and stroked her arm. She
would have touched her breast where he had touched it, but the
eyes of the congregation were upon her.

Flesh, flesh, flesh, said the vicar.

His son, scouting in the fields for a mole's hill or the signs of a
red fox, whistling to the birds and patting the calves as they
stood untimid at their mother's sides, came upon a dead rabbit
sprawling on a stone. The rabbit's head was riddled with
pellets, the dogs had torn open its belly, and the marks of a
ferret's teeth were upon its throat. He lifted it gently up,

tickling it behind the ears. The blood from its head dropped on his hand. Through the rip in the belly, its intestines had dropped out and coiled on the stone. He held the little body close to his jacket, and ran home through the fields, the rabbit dancing against his waistcoat. As he reached the gate of the vicarage, the worshippers dribbled out of church. They shook hands and raised their hats, smiling at the poor boy with his long green hair, his ass's ears, and death buttoned under his jacket. He was always the poor boy to them.

Rhys Rhys sat in his study, the stem of his pipe stuck between his flybuttons, the bible unopened upon his knees. The day of God was over, and the sun, like another sabbath, went down behind the hills. He lit the lamp, but his own oil burned brighter. He drew the curtains, shutting out the unwelcome night. But he opened his own heart up, and the bald pulse that beat there was a welcome stranger. He had not felt love like this since the woman who scratched him, seeing the woman witch in his male eyes, had fallen into his arms and kissed him, and whispered Welsh words as he took her. She had been the mother of his daughter and had died in her pains, stealing, when she was dead, the son of his second love, and leaving the greenhaired changeling in its place. Merry with desire, Rhys Rhys cast the bible on the floor. He reached for another book, and read, in the lamplit darkness, of the old woman who had deceived the devil. The devil is poor flesh, said Rhys Rhys.

His son came in, bearing the rabbit in his arms. The lank, redcoated boy was a flesh out of the past. The skin of the unburied dead patched to his bones, the smile of the changeling on his mouth, and the hair of the sea rising from his scalp, he stood before Rhys Rhys. A ghost of his mother, he held the rabbit gently to his breast, rocking it to and fro. Cunningly, from under halfclosed lids, he saw his father shrink away from the vision of death. Be off with you, said Rhys Rhys. Who was this green stranger to carry in death and rock it, like a baby under a warm shawl of fur, before him? For a minute the flesh of the world lay still; the old terror set in; the waters of the breast dried up; the nipples grew through the sand. Then he drew his hand over his eyes, and only the rabbit remained, a little sack of flesh, half empty, swaying in the arms of his son.

Be off, he said. The boy held the rabbit close, and rocked it, and tickled it again.

Changeling, said Rhys Rhys. He is mine, said the boy, I'll peel him and keep the skull. His room in the attic was crowded with skulls and dried pelts, and little bones in bottles.

Give it to me.

He is mine.

Rhys Rhys tore the rabbit away, and stuffed it deep in the pocket of his smoking coat. When his daughter came in, dressed and ready for bed, with a candle in her hand, Rhys Rhys had death in his pocket.

She was timid, for his touch still ached on her arm and breast but she bent unblushing over him. Saying good-night, she kissed him, and he blew her candle out. She was smiling as he lowered the wick of the lamp.

Step out of your shift, said he. Shiftless, she stepped towards his arms.

I want the little skull, said a voice in the dark.

From his room at the top of the house, through the webs on the windows, and over the furs and the bottles, the boy saw a mile of green hill running away into the darkness of the first dawn. Summer storm in the heat of the rain, flooring the grassy mile, had left some new morning brightness, out of the dead night, in each reaching root.

Death took hold of his sister's legs as she walked through the calf-deep heather up the hill. He saw the high grass at her thighs. And the blades of the upgrowing wind, out of the four windsmells of the manuring dead, might drive through the soles of her feet, up the veins of the legs and stomach, into her womb and her pulsing heart. He watched her climb. She stood, gasping for breath, on a hill of the wider hill, tapping the wall of her bladder, fondling her matted chest (for the hair grew on her as on a grown man), feeling the heart in her wrist, loving her coveted thinness. She was to him as ugly as the sowfaced woman Llareggub who had taught him the terrors of the flesh. He remembered the advances of that unlovely woman. She blew out his candle as he stepped towards her on the night the great hail had fallen and he had hidden in her rotting house from the cruelty of the weather. Now half a mile off his sister stood in the morning, and the vermin of the hill might spring upon her as she stood, uncaring, rounding the angles of her ugliness. He smiled at the thought of the devouring rats, and looked around the room for a bottle to hold her heart. Her skull, fixed by a socket to the nail above his bed, would be a smiling welcome to the first pains of waking.

But he saw Rhys Rhys stride up the hill, and the bowl of his sister's head, fixed invisibly above his sheets, crumbled away. Standing straight by the side of a dewy tree, his sister beckoned. Up went Rhys Rhys through the calfdeep heather, the death in the grass, over the boulders and up through the reaching ferns, to where she stood. He took her hand. The two shadows linked hands, and climbed together to the top of the hill. The boy saw them go, and turned his face to the wall as they vanished, in one dull shadow, over the edge, and down to the dingle at the west foot of the lovers' alley.

Later, he remembered the rabbit. He ran downstairs and found it in the pocket of the smoking coat. He held death against him, tasting a cough of blood upon his tongue as he climbed, contented, back to the bright bottles and the wall of heads.

In the first dew of light he saw his father clamber for her white hand. She who was his sister walked with a swollen belly over the hill. She touched him between the legs, and he sighed and sprang at her. But the nerves of her face mixed with the quiver in his thighs, and she shot from him. Rhys Rhys, over the bouldered rim, led her to terror. He sighed and sprang at her. She mixed with him in the fourth and the fifth terrors of the flesh. Said Rhys Rhys, Your mother's eyes. It was not her eyes that saw him proud before her, nor the eyes in her thumb. The lashes of her fingers lifted. He saw the ball under the nail.

It was, they said, on a fine sabbath morning in the early spring that she bore him a male child. Brought to bed of her father, she screamed for an anaesthetic as the knocking head burst through. In her gown of blood she slept until twilight, and a star burst bloody through each ear. With a scissors and rag, Rhys Rhys attended her, and, gazing on the shrivelled features and the hands like the hands of a mole, he gently took the child away, and his daughter's breast cried out and ran into the mouth of the surrounding shadow. The shadow pouted for the milk and the binding cottons. The child spat in his arms, the noise of the running air was blind in its ears, and the deaf light died from its eyes.

Rhys Rhys, with the dead child held against him, stepped into the night, hearing the mother moan in her sleep and the deadly shadow, filled sick with milk, flowing around the house. He turned his face towards the hills. A shadow walked close to him and, silent in the shadow of a full tree, the changeling waited. He made an image for the moon, and the flesh of the moon fell away, leaving a star-eyed skull. Then with a smile he ran back over the lawns and into the crying house. Half way up the stairs, he heard his sister die. Rhys Rhys climbed on.

On the top of the hill he laid the baby down, and propped it against the heather. Death propped the dark flowers. The baby stiffened in the rigor of the moon. Poor flesh, said Rhys Rhys as he pulled at the dead heather and furze. Poor angel, he said to the listening mouth of the baby. The fruit of the flesh falls with the worm from the tree. Conceiving the worm, the bark crumbles. There lay the poor star of flesh that had dropped, like the bead of a woman's milk through the nipples of a wormy tree.

He stacked the torn heathers in the midst of the circle where the stones still howled on the sabbaths. On the head of the purple stack, he piled the dead grass. A stack of death, the heather grew as tall as he, and loomed at last over his windy hair.

Behind a boulder moved the accompanying shadow, and the shadow of the boy was printed under the fiery flank of a tree. The shadow marked the boy, and the boy marked the bones of the naked baby under their chilly cover, and how the grass scraped on the bald skull, and where his father picked out a path in the cancerous growths of the silent circle. He saw Rhys Rhys pick up the baby and place it on the top of the stack, saw the head of a burning match, and heard the crackle of the bush, breaking like a baby's arm.

The stack burst into flame. Rhys Rhys, before the red eye of the creeping fire, stretched out his arms and beckoned the shadow from the stones. Surrounded by shadows, he prayed before the flaming stack, and the sparks of the heather blew past his smile. Burn, child, poor flesh, mean flesh, flesh, flesh, sick sorry flesh, flesh of the foul womb, burn back to dust, he prayed.

And the baby caught fire. The flames curled round its mouth and blew upon the shrinking gums. Flame round its red cord lapped its little belly till the raw flesh fell upon the heather.

A flame touched its tongue. Eeeeeh, cried the burning baby, and the illuminated hill replied.

THE END OF THE RIVER

From *New English Weekly*, vol. 6, no. 6 (November 1934), pp. 132–4.

Twelve generations of the Quincey family, that dogfaced line, had left their mark upon the manor. The walls remained steadfast, but covered with a green fungus that sprouted upon the Quincey habitations, regardless of pruning. The gardener had not neglected the lawns, and the flower-beds, though pale and blowsy, were tended with all his senile care, for Chubb could never die, bound, as he was, so inextricably to the Quincey bosom. But weeds grew thick where weeds were little expected to grow. Ivy climbed up the walls of the coach house, and, in spite of the daily attentions of the youngest housemaid but one, moss invaded the front steps and rust lay thick upon the knocker. Hens upon the bird-limed patch beyond the kitchen died at a premature age, while the eggs they contrived to lay were rarely oval and often of a withered shape and a rather unpleasant mottled colour. The pigs were fed as heartily as pigs could wish, but they grew thin and died. The cows' milk tasted like vinegar.

The Quincey manor, with its portrait gallery of canine gentlemen, its dining-hall furnished in three periods, and its perilous verandahs from which the bloodless Quinceys, on midsummer nights, would pass their gravish comments on the moon, had resolved to crumble, spurning renovations and improvements, sitting on the camel hill over the disagreeable river, waiting for its end.

And Sir Peregrine, twelfth baron, had nothing but sympathy for it. It had sheltered twelve generations of doggy aristocrats and their litters, had seen small boys grow to be small men, had seen them meet, mate, and lie, at last, in the depths of the family vault, their dead paws on their chests. It had entertained near-royalty, and consequently had allotted a royal bedroom to its left wing. Over all the passions of a most impure world it had spread its painted roofs, and, on one notable occasion, had hidden, in a cellar full of stale wine and rats, the murdered body of poor Sir Thomas.

The manor, thought Sir Peregrine, was old enough to die, had pondered enough upon the human follies and felt no fear of death.

Stroking a three-days' beard, he placed a deck-chair on the safest part of the verandah, looked up into the sun and turned to the year 1889 in the Quincey Chronicles.

Somewhere a romantic daughter spelt out her Sunday music. His lady, in the quiet of her room, was writing to an Australian cousin. In his apartment the butler was reading from the literary pages of the *Observer*. Chubb, in the not very far distance, leaned on a garden gate and smoked.

Peregrine, read the twelfth baron from the Chronicles, took up the title on the death of his father, Belphigor, in 1889. In 1902 he married the Honourable Katerina Hautley, second daughter of Lord and Lady Winch of Alltheway Park, Gloucestershire. From this union were born three daughters: Katerina, who died of influenza in her second year, Astasia, and Phoebe Mary. Sir Peregrine was a colonel in the Territorial Army up to the Great War (1914–1918), and an official in the Ministry of War during those troubled years. He was elected Master of the Tidhampton Hunt in 1920, following upon the death of Alderman Alcock, and in 1922 broke his arm while riding with the hounds. In the following year Phoebe Mary married the Honourable Douglas Dougal, son of Sir Douglas and Lady Dougal of Halfandhalf Castle, Perth. In 1924 Phoebe Mary died in childbirth.

That was all. The Chronicles of the previous Quincey generations were written in detail and with an ornamentation of style that did credit to the literary accomplishments of the family. But Sir Peregrine dealt in facts, and facts alone. His life until that moment, but shorn of its hopes and foolishness, its strength and weaknesses, delights and dolours, spread over half a page of the ponderous book. This little life set between the eccentricities of the longwinded Belphigor and . . .

Sir Peregrine put the book down.

Chubb was still leaning and smoking. The smoke rose up

vertically into the windless air. Chubb had not moved. His eyes rested on the river which went Sir Peregrine knew not where, meandering, he supposed, through a world of fields and rushes, making noise over pebbles, till it came to a sudden stop. He had always called it the one river that did not wind safely to the sea.

Astasia had stopped her playing.

Life was good, he found, on most Sunday afternoons. But to-day he was restless, and could not sit, as he had for so many years, dreamily upon the verandah, feeling the world grow and hum around him, hearing the music of a sweetly untuned piano or the songs of birds.

The day was beautiful. Clouds sailed on the sky. There was a warm sun. He looked down to where the Chronicles lay at his feet, and knew, quite suddenly and almost happily, all that was the matter. The time had come for the dissolution of the Quinceys, for the fall of their manor and the end of their dynasty.

Sir Peregrine, lifting the book, took out a pencil used to a stump through the solving of innumerable crossword puzzles.

In 1924 he read again, Phoebe Mary died in childbirth.

Phoebe Mary had been his favourite daughter. He had cried for six nights after she was buried. Then he, too, had buried her, under the clouds and mists of his mind. Once he had forgotten her name. Phoebe Mary? he said, and had fallen to wondering who that could be with such a name.

Phoebe Mary died in childbirth.

The end of the Quinceys, he wrote with the pencil.

Then he added the date.

In the garden he looked around him, at the flowers whose colours were as even as those in a toy paint box. The little wind there was moved the petals so that they seemed, to him, to breathe for the last time the sweet air of the surrounding beds. He knew they were aware of climax, and loved them for their serenity. Chubb had nurtured them, and the end of the world would see the gardener like a god, waiting in a woman's blue smock, for his reward.

The end of the world was the end of the manor. And Chubb, though he would say nothing of it, neither affirm nor contradict, had tended the first bed for the first young baron.

Sir Peregrine found him at the end of the path. The gardener did not move. His arms were resting on the gate that led to the seven fields going down to the river.

Sir Peregrine, wiping a remnant of dinner from his ancient waistcoat, looked down to where the water rolled over the dirty stones. At the end of the water was the end of everything. Today he was to walk over the fields and follow the river where it went, through towns or countries, over hills or under, until the sudden stop.

The garden was humming behind them.

The clouds moved on softly to some stop.

How old are you, Chubb? asked Sir Peregrine. You were the gardener here when Lady Astasia rode to her Queen, Elizabeth, over the rocky roads on a piebald horse. You tended the flowers when Quentin, third of the Quinceys, wrote to his lady in an ivory tower, wrapping the verses round a pigeon's throat. At Christmas you made snowmen for me. How many years have you brooded over the dirty river? You always knew the end of all things lay where it stopped. I only knew to-day. It came to me suddenly and I knew.

The immortal Chubb made no answer. He tilted his felt hat further back on his head, and sent up a ring of smoke from a white pipe. His face, fringed with a yellowing beard, was as round and expressionless as a saucer. At any time a breath of wind might send another crack along its surface, and make a thousand smiles or frowns. Through a space in his teeth he breathed and whistled, and made a succession of mysterious tunes as he drew at his pipe.

The exterior Chubb belied what was divine beneath. He looked like nothing more than an ancient gardener, with his woman's smock pinned untidily around him.

Chubb, I am going.

Sir Peregrine waited for the words to pierce the gardener's smoky armour.

I am going to follow the river to its end. Tell me one word of cheer before I go. Say good-bye, undying Chubb.

The birds, said the gardener, 'ave 'ad the seeds.

It was enough. Sir Peregrine climbed quickly over the gate and ran down the field. At the end was a stile. He climbed it, and ran again over the uneven grass, his hair leaping about his head and his brass-buttoned waistcoat flapping against his sides. Three fields. Four fields. Sweat ran down his forehead on to his neck and collar. He could hear his heart thundering in his ears. But he kept at the same crazy jog, over another stile, along another field, stopping to climb through a small hole in the hedge, then on again, snorting and blowing.

A crow, perched on a scarecrow's shoulder, suddenly started cawing as the twelfth baron galloped past, then flew above him, spurring him on with harsh cries.

Now he could hear the noise of the river. On the low bank above it, he stared down on to the little fishes and the shining pebbles. The crow, seeing him stop, gave a final sardonic caw, and flew back to its lone companion, who was swinging a ragged arm in the wind.

Sie Peregrine felt a great elation surging through him. He turned around, and saw the Quincey manor, on its imperial hill, squinting down upon him. He followed the river bank through the dirty fields and through a wood brown with owls' wings. He saw the sun lowering in the sky. Now he no longer ran, but stumbled over the fields, his eyes dim, covered in tears, half unseeing. His clothes were damp about him. His hair that had, in the mad run down the seven fields, leapt so proudly on his head, straggled on to his wet brow. He was thirsty and tired. But he stumbled on.

Where does the river end? he called out to an old woman driving cows over a green field.

Where does it end? he asked. But the hedges and the ferns and the talking pebbles never replied.

He came at last to a well by the side of a meadow, and there a girl-child was washing clothes. He saw her through his tears and heard her voice singing.

Is this the end?

Yes, said the girl-child.

The end, said Sir Peregrine in a whisper. The end of the manor, the Quinceys, and me.

The words made such a nice little rhythm that he started to sing them in his old voice.

The end of the manor, the Quinceys and me.

The child was frightened.

For twelve generations, he said, the Quinceys have lived their little lives up there. And he pointed with a bewildered hand towards the sky. This is the end, he said.

Yes, said the child.

What is the end? he said. What have you to give? What at the end?

He held his arms out.

With a frightened cry, the girl-child thrust an un-washed napkin into his hand. He clasped it, and she ran away. Not looking, but holding it to his breast and making soft, delighted noises in his throat, Sir Peregrine lay down upon the grass. The moon came up. Chubb had not failed.

And that immortal gardener, as the twelfth baron lay down on a bed of grass and soft manure, was smoking a white pipe in the quiet of the Quincey gardens. Sunday was almost passed, and then there would be another day. Contentedly the ancient gardener, in his woman's smock, leaned on the garden gate and smoked.

THE HORSE'S HA

From *Janus*, no. 2 (May 1936), pp. 4–9.

He saw the plague enter the village on a white horse. It was a cancerous horseman, with a furuncle for a hat, that galloped the beast over grass and cobble and the coloured hill. Plague, plague, cried Tom Twp as the horse on the horizon, scenting the stars, lifted a white head. Out came the grocer with an egg in his hand, and the butcher in a bloody coat. They followed the line of the lifted finger, but the horse had gone, the trees were no speakers, and the birds who flew criss-cross on the sky said no word of warning to the parson's rookery or the chained starlings in the parlour of ApLlewelyn. As white, said Tom Twp, as the egg in your hand. He remembered the raw head of the horseman, and whispered slyly, As red as mother's rump in your window. The clouds darkened, the sun went in, the suddenly ferocious wind broke down three fences, and the cows, blue-eyed with plague, nibbled at the centres of the marrow beds. The egg fell, and the red yolk struggled between the spaces of the cobbles, the white mixed with the rain that dripped from the scarlet coat. In went the grocer with a stained hand, and the butcher among the hands of veal. Tom Twp, following his finger towards the horizon where the horse of plague had stamped and vanished, reached the dark church as the rain grew sick of the soil and drew back to heaven. He ran between the graves where the worm rubbed in the tradesman's hands. Mrs. ApLlewelyn raised a stone breast above the grass. Softly opening the door, he came upon the parson praying for disarmament in the central aisle. Disarm the forces of the army and the navy, he heard the parson murmur to the Christ of stained glass who smiled like a nannygoat above him, hearing the cries from Cardiff and the smoking West. Disarm the territorial

35

forces, the parson prayed. In anger, God smote him. There is plague, said Tom Twp. ApLlewelyn in the organ loft reached for the bass stops. The white plague drifted through the church to the music of the savage voluntary. Parson and sinner stood beneath the reflections of the Holy Family, marking in each ginger halo the hair of blood. There was to one the voice of an arming God in the echo of each chord, and, to the other, the horse's ha.

One by one the starlings died; the last remaining bird, with a pain in its crop, whistled at the late afternoon. ApLlewelyn, returning from music and marvelling at the sky, heard the last starling's voice as he walked up the drive. Why is there no welcome, wondered the keeper, from my starling charges. Every day of the year they had lost their tempers, tore at the sashes of the window watching on the flying world; they had scraped on the glass, and fetched up their wings from the limed bar, signalling before him. On the rug at his feet lay six starlings, cold and stiff, the seventh mourning. Death in his absence had laid six singers low. He who marks the sparrows fall has no time for my birds, said ApLlewelyn. He smote big, bloody death, and death, relenting, pulled a last fart from the bodies of the dead birds.

Plague, plague, cried Tom Twp, standing in a new rain. Where the undertaker's house had died in the trees, he holla'd, like ApLlewelyn, of big, bloody death; he heard the rooks cawing in the trees, and saw a galloping shadow. The trees smelt of opium and mice, to Tom two sorts of the hell-headed animal who ran in the skirtings of the grave. There were, on the branches of the trees and hanging upright from the earth, the owls that ate the mice and the mouths of the rosy flowers that fed on opium. To the chimneys of Last House and the one illuminated window he called the plague. Out came the undertaker in a frock coat; distrusting the light of the moon, he carried a candle in his gloved hand, the candle casting three shadows. To the middle shadow Tom Twp addressed his words of the white coming. Shall I measure, said the shadow on the left, the undead of Wales? Plague on a horse, said Tom Twp to the left shadow, and heard the darker shadow on the right reply.

No drug of man works on the dead. The parson, at his pipe,

sucked down a dead smoke from the nostrils of the travelling
horse who now, on a far-off mountain, neighed down at Africa.
Smitted by God, the parson, as the dark rose deepest where the
moon rose in a blaze of light, counted his blessings, the blazing
fire, the light in the tobacco, and the shape of the deep bowl.
Hell was this fire, the dark denial burning like a weed, and the
poppy out of the smoking earth. The lines of the bowl, that
patterned his grave, were the lines of the weedy world; the light
in the tobacco faded; the weed was at the parson's legs, worry-
ing him into a longer fall than the fall from heaven, and,
heavier than the poppy, into a long sleep.

Butcher and baker fell asleep that night, their women
sleeping at their sides. Butcher and baker took their women in
no image; their women broke again for them the accustomed
maidenheads, their erected saviours crossing, in my language,
the hill of hairs. Over the shops, the cold eggs that had life, the
box where the rats worked all night on the high meat, the shop-
keepers gave no thought to death. They felt, in the crowded
space between hip and belly, the action of a third lover. Death,
in the last gristle, broke on the minutes, and, by twelve beneath
Cathmarw steeple, the towers fell.

Shall I measure the undead? This, said the undertaker in his
parlour, pointing through the uncurtained window to the shape
of the night, is the grave for the walking and the breathing.
Here lay the sleepy body, the smoking body, the flesh that
burned a candle, and the lessening manwax. Go home and die,
he had told Tom Twp, and, telling it again to the mad moon,
he remembered the story of the resurrection-men who had
snatched a talking body out of the Cathmarw yards. He heard
the dead die round him, and a live man, in his grafted suit,
break up the gravel on the drive of Last House. Cathmarw, in
a bath of blood, slept still for the light day, Tom twisted in the
hedge, butcher and baker stiff by their loves, and parson with a
burnt-out pipe loose in his jaws. ApLlewelyn skinned the six
starlings; he dropped to the ground at last, holding two
handfuls of red and broken feathers; the seventh bird, naked as
its dead mates, still shivering, sang on the limed bar. Plague is
upon us, said Mr. Montgomery, the undertaker, for the wind
was resounding with the noise of departure, and the smell of the
departing flesh crept up the wind. In the skin of this Western

Wales, through the veins of the county, the rub of the plague transformed into a circle of sick and invisible promise the globe of seeds; swollen in the tubers of the trees, death poisoned the green buds and coloured the birthmarks of the forest with a fresh stain. Mr. Montgomery threw his glass of vinegar in the plague's face; the glass broke on the window, and the vinegar ran down the broken panes. He cardboarded each slit and crack, smelling the running acid as he nailed up a cloth to shield night from him; he bolted and barred the doors of his wooden house and stuffed the holes in the parlour corners, until, buried at last in a coffin with chimneys, he took down his mother's book. Cures for the sickness of the body and the sickness of the mind, ingredients for a saucer for resurrection, calls to the dead, said Bronwen Montgomery. The hand that wrote squarely to the crowded planet held a worm, and rain beat down the letters of her living name, and of Cathmarw's plague she said, in a translated tongue, that the horse was a white beast ridden over the hill by a raw-headed horseman. Take, said Bronwen, the blood of a bird, and mix it with the stuff of man. Take, of a dead man and bird, a bowl of death, and pour the bird's blood and the mortal sap through the sockets of the bowl. Stir with a finger, and, if a dead finger, drink my brew by me. He cast her aside. There was a bird and man in the unbolted darkness, plague in the loin and feather tickling the flesh and bone, uplifted fingers in the trees, and an eye in the air. These were his common visions; plague could not cloud the eye, nor the wind in the trees split the finger-nail. Unbolting, unbarring the coffin with chimneys, he walked into the single vision of the night; the night was one bird's blood, one pocket of man, one finger lifted in the many and the upward world. He walked through the woods and onto the dusty road that led to Wales all ways, to the left, to the right, to the north, to the south, down through the vegetations, and up through the eye of the air. Looking at the still trees in the darkness, he came at last to the house of ApLlewelyn. He opened the gate and walked up the drive. There, in the parlour, lay ApLlewelyn, six featherless starlings at his side, the seventh mourning. Take, take, said Bronwen out of the Cathmarw yards, the blood of a bird. He gathered a dead bird up, tore at its throat, and caught the cold blood in his hands. Drink my brew by me, said

Bronwen at his ear. He found a cup on the dresser, and half filled it with the blood of the shrunken starling. Though he rot he must wait, said Mr. Montgomery to the organist, till I drink her brew by her. Take, take, said his mother, the stuff of man. He hurried out and on, hearing the last starling mourn for the new departure.

Tom Twp was twisted in the hedge. He did not feel the jack-knife at his finger, and the going of the grassy wedding ring around it did not trouble him at all.

Parson, dead in his chair, did not cry aloud as his trousers slid down to his boots, and promise filled the bladder of a fountain-pen.

The cup was full. Mr. Montgomery stirred it with a wedding finger, and drank from it in the Cathmarw yards by the grave of his mother. Down went the red brew. The graves spun around him, the angels shifted on their stones, and the lids, invisible to the silent drinker, creaked on their hinges. Poison stirred him and he spun, one foot in his mother's grave. Dead Cathmarw made a movement out of the wooden hamlet towards the hill of hairs. The hair rose on his scalp. Blood in his blood, and the cold ounce of the parson's seed edgeing to creation, he counted the diminishings of the moon; the stationary sun slipped down, and the system he could not take to the ground broke in half and in a hundred stars. Three days went by in a wind, the fourth rising cloudless and sinking again to too many strokes from the out-counted steeple. The fourth night got up like a man; the vision altering, a woman in the moon lit up the yards. He counted the diminishings of the sun. Too many days, he said, sick of his mother's brew and of the poisoned hours that passed and repassed him, leaving on the gravel path a rag and a bone in a faded frock coat. But as the days passed, so the dead grew tired of waiting. Tom, uneasy in the hedge, raised a four-fingered hand to stifle the yawn that broke up the last remaining skins upon his face. Butcher and baker ached in too long a love, and cursed the beds that bore them. The six naked starlings rose on their wings, the seventh singing, and ApLlewelyn, out of a deep sleep, drifted into a reawakened world where the birds danced about him. So, tired of waiting, the dead rose and sought the undertaker, for the rot had set in, and their flesh fell as they walked, in a strange procession, along the dusty road that led all ways to the graves of Cathmarw.

Mr. Montgomery saw them come, and, as a new sunshine descended on the yards, offered them his cup of brew. But the dead refused his hand. Tom Twp hunched, the sterile parson, butcher and baker ungainly in their loves, and ApLlewelyn with his hands around the feathers, clawed at the earth, making a common grave. Far, far above them, the seven naked starlings scratched on the sky. A darkness descended on the yards, but lifted again as Mr. Montgomery questioned the parson as to the God of death. What is God's death? Lifting his head from the soil, the parson said, God took my promise. And he smote the earth. I am your tombmaker, said Mr. Montgomery as the unshrouded parson climbed into the grave. I, I took your promise, he said as the soil closed over. What is death's music? one note or many? the chord of contagion? Thus questioned the undertaker, the cup three quarters empty in his gloved hand. He who marks the sparrows fall has no time for my birds, said ApLlewelyn. What music is death? What should I know of the music of death who am no longer the keeper of birds? ApLlewelyn vanished into the second quarter of the grave. I, I slew your birds, said the undertaker to the vanishing man. The butcher was dead meat. Let me answer your platitudes, said the butcher's wife, scrubbing the surface of the double hole in the earth. I was love, I am dead, and my man still walks in me. What is death's love? said the undertaker to the woman. Let me answer your platitudes, said the grocer's wife. I was dead, I am love, and my man still treads in me. They who filled and were filled, in a two-backed death, filled the third quarter. And Tom Twp, counting his fingers at the edge of their acre, found a tenth miraculous finger, with a nail red as blood and a clear half-moon, Death is my last finger, said Tom Twp, and dived into the closing grave. So Mr. Montgomery was left alone, by the desolate church, under a disappearing moon. One by one the stars went out, leaving a hole in heaven. He looked upon the grave, and slowly removed his coat.

THE SCHOOL FOR WITCHES

From *Contemporary Poetry and Prose*, no. 4/5 (August–September 1936), pp. 95–100.

On Cader Peak there was a school for witches where the doctor's daughter, teaching the unholy cradle and the devil's pin, had seven country girls. On Cader Peak, half ruined in an enemy weather, the house with a story held the seven girls, the cellar echoing, and a cross reversed above the entrance to the inner rooms. Here the doctor, dreaming of illness, in the centre of the tubercular hill, heard his daughter cry to the power swarming under the West roots. She invoked a particular devil, but the gehenna did not yawn under the hill, and the day and the night continued with their two departures; the cocks crew and the corn fell in the villages and yellow fields as she taught the seven girls how the lust of man, like a dead horse, stood up to his injected mixtures. She was short and fat-thighed; her cheeks were red; she had red lips and innocent eyes. But her body grew hard as she called to the black flowers under the tide of roots; when she fetched the curdlers out of the trees to bore through the cows' udders, the seven staring stared at the veins hardening in her breast; she stood uncovered, calling the devil, and the seven uncovered closed round her in a ring.

Teaching them the intricate devil, she raised her arms to let him enter. Three years and a day had vanished since she first bowed to the moon, and, maddened by the mid light, dipped her hair seven times in the salt sea, and a mouse in honey. She stood, still untaken, loving the lost man; her fingers hardened on light as on the breastbone of the unentering devil.

Mrs. Price climbed up the hill, and the seven saw her. It was the first evening of the new year, the wind was motionless on Cader Peak, and a half red, promising dusk floated over the rocks. Behind the midwife the sun sank as a stone sinks in a

41

marsh, the dark bubbled over it, and the mud sucked it down into the bubble of the bottomless fields.

In Bethlehem there is a prison for mad women, and in Cathmarw by the parsonage trees a black girl screamed as she laboured. She was afraid to die like a cow on the straw, and to the noises of the rooks. She screamed for the doctor on Cader Peak as the tumultuous West moved in its grave. The midwife heard her. A black girl rocked in her bed. Her eyes were stones. Mrs. Price climbed up the hill, and the seven saw her.

Midwife, midwife, called the seven girls. Mrs. Price crossed herself. A chain of garlic hung at her throat. Carefully, she touched it. The seven cried aloud, and ran from the window to the inner rooms where the doctor's daughter, bent on uncovered knees, counselled the black toad, her familiar, and the divining cat slept by the wall. The familiar moved its head. The seven danced, rubbing the white wall with their thighs until the blood striped the thin symbols of fertility upon them. Hand in hand they danced among dark symbols, under the charts that marked the rise and fall of the satanic seasons, and their white dresses swung around them. The owls commenced to sing, striking against the music of the suddenly awaking winter. Hand in hand the dancers spun around the black toad and the doctor's daughter, seven stags dancing, their antlers shaking, in the confusion of the unholy room.

She is a very black woman, said Mrs. Price, and curtsied to the doctor.

He woke to the midwife's story out of a dream of illness, remembering the broken quicked, the black patch and echo, the mutilated shadows of the seventh sense.

She lay with a black scissor-man.

He wounded her deep, said the doctor, and wiped a lancet on his sleeve.

Together they stumbled down the rocky hill.

A terror met them at the foot, the terror of the blind tapping their white sticks and the stumps of the arms on the solid darkness; two worms in the foil of a tree, bellies on the rubber sap and the glues of a wrong-grained forest, they, holding tight to hats and bags, crawled now up the path that led to the black birth. From right, from left, the cries of labour came in under

the branches, piercing the dead wood, from the earth where a
mole sneezed, and from the sky, out of the worms' sight.

They were not the only ones caught that night in the torrential blindness; to them, as they stumbled, the land was
empty of men, and the prophets of bad weather alone walked in
their neighbourhoods. Three tinkers appeared out of silence by
the chapel wall. Capel Cader, said the panman. Parson is down
on tinkers, said John Bucket. Cader Peak, said the scissor-man,
and up they went. They passed the midwife close; she heard the
scissors clacking, and the branch of a tree drum on the buckets.
One, two, three, they were gone, invisibly shuffling as she
hugged her skirts. Mrs. Price crossed herself for the second time
that day, and touched the garlic at her throat. A vampire with
a scissors was a Pembroke devil. And the black girl screamed
like a pig.

Sister, raise your right hand. The seventh girl raised her right
hand. Now say, said the doctor's daughter, Rise up out of the
bearded barley. Rise out of the green grass asleep in Mr.
Griffith's dingle. Big man, black man, all eye, one tooth, rise up
out of Cader marshes. Say the devil kisses me. The devil kisses
me, said the girl cold in the centre of the kitchen. Kiss me out
of the bearded barley. Kiss me out of the bearded barley. The
girls giggled in a circle. Swive me out of the green grass. Swive
me out of the green grass. Can I put on my clothes now? said
the young witch, after encountering the invisible evil.

Throughout the hours of the early night, in the smoke of the
seven candles, the doctor's daughter spoke of the sacrament of
darkness. In her familiar's eyes she read the news of a great and
an unholy coming; divining the future in the green and sleepy
eyes, she saw, as clearly as the tinkers saw the spire, the towering coming of a beast in stag's skin, the antlered animal whose
name read backwards, and the black, black, black wanderer
climbing a hill for the seven wise girls of Cader. She woke the
cat. Poor Bell, she said, smoothing his fur the wrong way. And,
Ding dong, Bell, she said, and swung the spitting cat.

Sister, raise your left hand. The first girl raised her left hand.
Now with your right hand put a needle in your left hand.
Where is a needle? Here, said the doctor's daughter, Is a needle,
here in your hair. She made a gesture over the black hair, and
drew a needle out from the coil at her ear. Say I cross you. I

cross you, said the girl, and, with the needle in her hand, struck at the black cat racked on the daughter's lap.

For love takes many shapes, cat, dog, pig, or goat; there was a lover, spellbound in the time of mass, now formed and featured in the image of the darting cat; his belly bleeding, he sped past the seven girls, past parlour and dispensary, into the night, on to the hill; the wind got at his wound, and swiftly he darted down the rocks, in the direction of the cooling streams.

He passed the three tinkers like lightning. Black cat is luck, said the panman. Bloody cat is bad luck, said John Bucket. The scissorman said nothing. They appeared out of silence by the wall of the Peak house, and heard a hellish music through the open door. They peered through the stained-glass window, and the seven girls danced before them. They have beaks, said the panman. Web feet, said John Bucket. The tinkers walked in.

At midnight the black girl bore her baby, a black beast with the eyes of a kitten and a stain at the corner of its mouth. The midwife, remembering birthmarks, whispered to the doctor of the gooseberry on his daughter's arm. Is it ripe yet? said Mrs. Price. The doctor's hand trembled, and his lancet cut the baby under the chin. Scream you, said Mrs. Price, who loved all babies.

The wind howled over Cader, waking the sleepy rooks who cawed from the trees and, louder than owls, disturbed the midwife's meditations. It was wrong for the rooks, those sleepy birds over the zinc roofs, to caw at night. Who put a spell on the rooks? The sun might rise at ten past one in the morning.

Scream you, said Mrs. Price, the baby in her arms, This is a wicked world. The wicked world, with a voice out of the wind, spoke to the baby half smothering under the folds of the midwife's overcoat. Mrs Price wore a man's cap, and her great breasts heaved under the black blouse. Scream you, said the wicked world, I am an old man blinding you, a wicked little woman tickling you, a dry death parching you. The baby screamed, as though a flea were on its tongue.

The tinkers were lost in the house, and could not find the inner room where the girls still danced with the beaks of birds upon them and their web feet bare on the cobblestones. The panman opened the dispensary door, but the bottles and the tray of knives alarmed him. The passages were too dark for

John Bucket, and the scissorman surprised him at a corner. Christ defend me, he cried. The girls stopped dancing, for the name of Christ rang in the outer halls. Enter, and, Enter, cried the doctor's daughter to the welcome devil. It was the scissorman who found the door and turned the handle, walking into candlelight. He stood before Gladwys on the threshold, a giant black as ink with a three days' beard. She lifted her face to his, and her sackcloth fell away.

Up the hill, the midwife, cooing as she came, held the newborn baby in her arms, and the doctor toiled behind her with his black bag rattling. The birds of the night flew by them, but the night was empty, and these restless wings and voices, hindering emptiness forever, were the feathers of shadows and the accents of an invisible flying. What purpose there was in the shape of Cader Peak, in the bouldered breast of the hill and the craters poxing the green-black flesh, was no more than the wind's purpose that willy nilly blew from all corners the odd turfs and stones of an unmoulded world. The grassy rags and bones of the steep hill were, so the doctor pondered as he climbed behind the baby rocking into memory on a strange breast, whirled together out of the bins of chaos by a winter wind. But the doctor's conceits came to nothing, for the black child let out a scream so high and loud that Mr. Griffiths heard it in his temple in the dingle. The worshipper of vegetables, standing beneath his holy marrow nailed in four places to the wall, heard the cry come down from the heights. A mandrake cried on Cader. Mr. Griffiths hastened in the direction of the stars.

John Bucket and the panman stepped into candlelight, seeing a strange company. Now in the centre circle of the room, surrounded by the unsteady lights, stood the scissorman and a naked girl; she smiled at him, he smiled at her, his hands groped for her body, she stiffened and slackened, he drew her close, smiling she stiffened again, and he licked his lips.

John Bucket had not seen him as a power for evil baring the breasts and the immaculate thighs of the gentlewomen, a magnetic blackman with the doom of women in his smile, forcing open the gates of love. He remembered a black companion on the roads, sharpening the village scissors, and, in the shadows, when the tinkers took the night, a coal-black shadow, silent as the travelling hedges.

Was this tall man, the panman murmured, who takes the doctor's daughter with no how-d'you-do, was he Tom the scissorman? I remember him on the highways in the heat of the sun, a black, three-coated tinker.

And, like a god, the scissorman bent over Gladwys, he healed her wound, she stood his ointment and his fire, she burned at the tower altar, and the black sacrifice was done. Stepping out of his arms, her offering cut and broken, the gut of a lamb, she smiled and cried manfully: Dance, dance, my seven. And the seven danced, their antlers shaking, in the confusion of the unholy room. A coven, a coven, cried the seven as they danced. They beckoned the panman from the door. He edged towards them, and they caught his hands. Dance, dance, my strange man, the seven cried. John Bucket joined them, his buckets drumming, and swiftly they dragged him into the rising fury of the dance. The scissorman in the circle danced like a tower. They sped round and round, none crying louder than the two tinkers in the heart of the swirling company, and lightly the doctor's daughter was among them. She drove them to a faster turn of foot; giddy as weathercocks in a hundred changing winds, they were revolving figures in the winds of their dresses and to the music of the scissors and the metal pans; giddily she spun between the dancing hoops, the wheels of cloth and hair, and the bloody ninepins spinning; the candles grew pale and lean in the wind of the dance; she whirled by the tinker's side, by the scissorman's side, by his dark, damp side, smelling his skin, smelling the seven furies.

It was then that the doctor, the midwife, and the baby entered through the open door as quietly as could be. Sleep well, Pembroke, for your devils have left you. And woe on Cader Peak that the black man dances in my house. There had been nothing for that savage evening but an end of evil. The grave had yawned, and the black breath risen up.

Here danced the metamorphoses of the dusts of Cathmarw. Lie level, the ashes of man, for the phoenix flies from you, woe unto Cader, into my nice, square house. Mrs. Price fingered her garlic, and the doctor stood grieving.

The seven saw them. A coven, a coven, they cried. One, dancing past them, snatched at the doctor's hand; another, dancing caught him around the waist; and, all bewildered by the white flesh of their arms, the doctor danced. Woe, woe on Cader, he cried as he swirled among maidens, and his steps gathered speed. He heard his voice rising; his feet skimmed over the silver cobbles. A coven, a coven, cried the dancing doctor, and bowed in his measures.

Suddenly Mrs. Price, hugging the black baby, was surrounded at the entrance of the room. Twelve dancers hemmed her in, and the hands of strangers pulled at the baby on her breast. See, see, said the doctor's daughter, The cross on the black throat. There was blood beneath the baby's chin where a sharp knife had slipped and cut. The cat, cried the seven, The cat, the black cat. They had unloosed the spellbound devil that dwelt in the cat's shape, the human skeleton, the flesh and heart out of the gehenna of the valley roots and the image of the creature calming his wound in the far-off streams. Their magic was done; they set the baby down on the stones, and the dance continued. Pembroke, sleep well, whispered the dancing midwife, Lie still, you empty county.

And it was thus that the last visitor that night found the thirteen dancers in the inner rooms of Cader House: a black man and a blushing girl, two shabby tinkers, a doctor, a midwife, and seven country girls, swirling hand in hand under the charts that marked the rise and fall of the satanic seasons, among the symbols of the darker crafts, giddily turning, raising their voices to the roofs as they bowed to the cross reversed above the inner entrance.

Mr Griffiths, half blinded by the staring of the moon, peeped in and saw them. He saw the newborn baby on the cold stones. Unseen in the shadow by the door, he crept towards the baby and lifted it to its feet. The baby fell. Patiently Mr. Griffiths lifted the baby to its feet. But the little mandrake would not walk that night.

THE HOLY SIX

From *Contemporary Poetry and Prose*, no. 9 (Spring 1937), pp. 18–26.

The Holy Six of Wales sat in silence. The day was drawing to a close, and the heat of the first discussion grew cooler with the falling sun. All through the afternoon they had talked of nothing but the disappearance of the rector of Llareggub, and now, as the first lack of light moved in a visible shape and colour through the room, and their tongues were tired, and they heard the voices in their nerves, they waited only for the first darkness to set in. At the first signs of night they would step from the table, adjust their hats and smiles, and walk into the wicked streets. Where the woman smiled under the lamps, and the promise of the old sickness stirred in the fingertips of the girls in the dark doorways, the Six would pass dreaming, to the scrape of their boots on the pavement, of the women throughout the town smiling and doctoring love. To Mr. Stul the women drifted in a maze of hair, and touched him in a raw place. The women drifted around Mr. Edger. He caught them close to him, holding their misty limbs to his with no love or fire. The women moved again, with the grace of cats, edging down the darker alleys where Mr. Vyne, envious of their slant-eyed beauty, would scrape and bow. To Mr. Rafe, their beauties, washed in blood, were enemies of the fluttering eyes, and moved, in what image they would, full-breasted, fur-footed, to a massacre of the flesh. He saw the red nails, and trembled. There was no purpose in the shaping wombs but the death of the flesh they shaped, and he shrank from the contact of death, and the male nerve was pulled alone. Tugging and tweaking, putting salt on the old love-cuts, Mr. Lucytre conducted an imaginary attack upon the maidenheads. How here and now there he ripped the women, and, kissing them, he bit into their lips. Spitefully, Mr. Stipe watched him. Down fell the women on the sharp blade, and his heart smiled within him as they rose to dress their wounds.

The holy life was a constant erection to these six gentlemen. Miss Myfanwy came in with a letter.

Mr. Edger opened the envelope. It contained a square piece of paper that might be a banknote. It was a letter from Mrs. Amabel Owen, and was written in a backward hand.

She put malignity in the curves and tails of the characters, a cloven foot, a fork, and a snake's sting coming out from the words in a separate life as the words lay back giddy from her revolving pen along the lines.

She, like Peter the poet, wrote of the Jarvis valley. But while she saw by each bare tree a barer ghost and the ghost of the last spring and summer, he saw the statue of the tree and no ghost but his own that whistled out of the sick bed and raced among seaward fields.

Here in the valley, wrote Mrs. Owen, my husband and I live quiet as two mice.

As she writes, thought Mr. Stul, she feels the weight of her breasts on her ink-black arm.

Do the holy gentlemen believe in ghosts?

With the chains of cloud and iron suspended from their limbs, thought Mr. Rafe, they would drip the deadly night-shade into my ear.

May she bear a vampire's baby, said Mr. Stipe. The Reverend Mr. Davies of Llareggub is staying with us for an indefinite period, she wrote in her secret hand.

Over the more level roadway on the lower hills, drawn in a jogcart by a sweating pony, the Holy Six journeyed in search of Mrs. Owen. Miss Myfanwy, seated uncomfortably between Mr. Stul and Mr. Lucytre, conscious of the exposure of her calf and the pressure of Mr. Lucytre's hand in the small of her back, prayed that the moon might not go in. There in the crowded cart the darkness would conceal the roving of the holy hands, and better Mr. Stul's delight.

The wheels of the cart bumped on a boulder.

Over we go, said Mr. Rafe, too frightened to brood upon the dissolution of his delicate body as it tumbled down the slope.

Over we go, said Mr. Vyne, thinking how hard it was that

death should come alone, the common flesh of Miss Myfanwy seated so near him.

As the cart balanced on one wheel, and the pony, with the entire weight on one back leg, pawed at the air with its hanging hooves, Mr. Stul thrust his hand high up under Miss Myfanwy's skirt, and Mr. Lucytre, smiling at destruction, drove his fingers into her back until the knuckles tingled and the invisible flesh reddened with pain. Mr. Edger clasped everything within reach, holding tight to his phallic hat. Mr. Stipe leant suddenly to one side. The pony slipped on the wet turf, whinnied, and fell. God is good, said old Vole the carter, and down he went, gathering speed, a white-haired boulder plunging into the craggy meadow fifty feet below. In one tight, black ball, the rest of the company rolled over the side. Is it blood? is it blood? cried Miss Myfanwy as they fell. Mr. Stul smiled, and fixed his arm more tightly round her.

On the grass below old Vole lay quietly on his back. He looked at the winter moon, that had not slipped, and the peace in the field. As six clerical hats and a draggled bonnet dropped near his feet, he turned on one side and saw the bodies of his passengers tumbling down upon him like a bony manna.

Darkness came for the second time. Now, with the hiding of the moon, the Holy Six arrived at the foot of the hills that separated the Jarvis valley from the fields of the wild land. The trees on those ridges were taller than any they had seen in their journey from the fatal meadow, greener and straighter than the trees in the town parks. There was a madman in each tree. This they did not know, seeing only the sanity of the trees on the broad back of the upper grasses. The hills, that had curved all day in the circle of light, now straightened out against the sky, in a hundred straight lines ascended to the clouds, and in one stark shadow blocked out the moon. Shifting along the properties of the soil, man's chemic blood, pulled from him by the warring wind, mixed with the dust that the holy gentlemen, like six old horses, stamped into a cloud. The dust lay thick on their black boots; on old Vole's beard it scraped, grey as water, between the ginger and the white; it drifted over Miss Myfanwy's patent boots and was lost in the cracks of her feet. For a minute they stood, trembling at the height of the hills. Then they adjusted their hats.

One behind the other they clambered upward, very far from the stars. The roots beneath their feet cried in the voices of the upspringing trees. It was to each member of the expedition a strange and a different voice that sounded along the branches. They reached the top of the hill, and the Jarvis valley lay before them. Miss Myfanwy smelt the clover in the grass, but Mr. Lucytre smelt only the dead birds. There were six vowels in the language of the branches. Old Vole heard the leaves. Their sentimental voice, as they clung together, spoke of the season of the storks and the children under the bushes. The Holy Six went down the hill, and the carter followed on the dark heels.

But, before they knew where they were, and before the tenth Jarvis field had groaned beneath them, and before Mrs. Owen spelt out their flesh and bone in the big ball on her table, morning suddenly came down; the meadows were oak-sided, standing greener than a sea as a lull came to the early light, lying under the wind as the south-west opened; the ancient boughs had all the birds of Wales upon them, and, from the farms among the trees and the fields on the unseen hillside, the cocks crew and the sheep cried. The wood before them, glowing from a bloody centre, burned like cantharides, a tuft of half-parting blooms and branches erect on the land that spouted up to the summits of the hills, angelically down, through ribbed throats of flowers and rising poisons, to the county's heart. The grass that was heavy with dew, though the crystals on each blade broke lightly, lay still as they walked, a woman's stillness under the thrust of man lying in the waking furze and the back of the bedded ribs of the hill's half heather, the halves of gold and green by the slope quarries staining a rich shire and a common soil. And it was early morning, and the world was moist, when the crystal-gazer's husband, a freak in knickerbockers with an open coppish and a sabbath gamp, came over the stones outside his house to meet the holy travellers.

His beard was wagging as he bowed. Your holiness, said Mr. Owen to the Six. Battered and bruised, the soles of their boots dragging like black and muddy wings along the ground, piously the Six responded. Mr. Owen bowed to Miss Myfanwy who, as his shirt wagged like a beard from his open trousers, curtsied low and blushed.

In the parlour, where Mrs. Owen had read out the bloody
coming, the Six gathered coldly round the fire, and two kettles
sang. An old and ragged man dragged in a tub. Where is the
mustard, Mr. Davies? questioned the crystal-gazer from her
chair in the darkest corner. Aware of her presence for the first
time, the Holy Six spun round, seeing the big ball move
inwardly, the unendurable head of evil, green as the woman's
eyes and blacker than the shadows pouched under the lower
lids, wriggle over the wet hint of hills at the globe's edges. She
was a tidy little body, with plump hands and feet, and a love-
curl glistened on her forehead; dressed, like a Sunday, in cold
and shining black, with a brooch of mother's ivory and a bone-
white bangle, she saw the Holy Six reflected as six solid
stumps, the amputated limbs of the deadly man who rotted in
her as she swayed before his eyes, before his twelve bright eyes
and the power of the staring Six.

Her womb and her throat and her hair.

Her green witch's eyes.

Her costly bangle.

The moles on her cheek.

Her young complexion.

The bones of her legs, her nails, her thumb.

The Six stood in front of her and touched her craftily, like the
old men with Susannah, and stared upon her where the unborn
baby stirred manfully in the eight month.

The old man returned with mustard.

This is the Reverend Mr. Davies of Llareggub, said Mrs.
Owen.

The Holy Six rubbed their hands.

These are the Holy Six of Wales.

Mr. Davies bowed, took off the kettles, half filled the tin tub,
and poured the mustard on to the boiling water. Mr. Owen,
appearing suddenly at his shoulder, gave him a yellow sponge.
Bewildered by the yellow water that sucked at the spoon, by the
dripping sponge in his fingers, and by the silence in the parlour,
Mr. Davies turned trembling to the holy gentlemen. A timeless
voice spoke in his ear, and a hand on his shrouded shoulder sank
through the collar-bone; a hand was on his heart, and the
intolerable blood-heat struck on a strong shadow. He knelt
down in the wilderness of the tiny parlour, and off came the

holy socks and boots. I, Davies, bathed their feet, muttered the
grey minister. So that he might remember, the old, mad man
said to himself, I, Davies, the poor ghost, washed the six sins in
mustard and water.

Light was in the room, the world of light, and the holy
Jewish word. On clock and black fire, light brought the inner
world to pass, and the shape in his image that changed with the
silent changes of the shape of light twisted his last man's-word.
The word grew like light. He loved and coveted the last, dark
light, turning from his memories to the yellow sea and the
prowed beak of the spoon. In the world of love, through the
drowning memories, he shifted one lover's smile to the mouth
of a naughty lover cruel to the slept-with dead who died before
dressing, and slowly turned to the illuminated face and the firer
of the dead. Touching Mr. Stul on the ankle, his ghost who
laboured—now he was three parts ghost, and his manhood
withered like the sap in a stick under a scarecrow's tatters—
leapt out to marry Mary; all-sexed and nothing, intangible
hermaphrodite riding the neuter dead, the minister of God in a
grey image mounted dead Mary. Mrs. Owen, wise to the
impious systems, saw through the inner eye that the round but
unbounded earth rotted as she ripened; a circle, not of her
witch's maging, grew around her; the immaculate circle
broadened, taking a generation's shape. Mr. Davies touched
the generation's edges; up rose the man-stalking seed; and the
circle broke. It was Mr. Stul, the horny man, the father of
Aberystwyth's bastards, who bounded over the broken circle,
and, hand in hand with the grey ghost, kissed on divinity until
the heavens melted.

The Holy five were not aware of this.

The lank-shanked Mr. Edger put out his right foot, and Mr.
Davies washed it; careful of the temperature of the water
rippling round the glassy skin, the minister of God washed the
left foot; he remembered poor Davies, poor ghostly Davies, the
man of bone and collar, howling, from a religious hill of the
infinite curve of matter and the sound of the unspoken word;
and, remembering Llareggub, the village with a rotting house,
he grasped at the fat memories, the relics of the flesh that hung
shabbily from him, and the undeniable desires; he grasped at
the last senile hair on the skull as windily the world broke

Davies up, and the ghost, having no greed or desire, came undead out of the particles.

Neither were the Holy four aware of this.

It was the foxy-whiskered Mr. Vyne who said out of the darkness to the ghost Davies: Beautiful is Mrs. Amabel Owen, the near-mother, the generation-bellied, from her teeth to her ten toes. My smile is a red hole, and my toes are like fingers. He sighed behind Mary and caught his breath at the seedy rim of the circle, seeing how beautiful she was as she shifted about him in the mothering middle of the earth. And out of the roots of the earth, lean as trees and whiter than the spring froth, rose her tall attendants. As the crystal-gazer and the virgin walked in one magic over their double grave, dead Davies and dead Vyne cried enviously: Beautiful is Amabel Mary, the ravished maiden, from her skull to her grave-walking feet.

Where but an hour earlier a far sea wind had blown the sun about, black night dropped down. Time on the clock denied the black coming.

Mr. Rafe was more frightened of the dark than anything else in the world. He watched, with wide, white eyes, the lighting of the parlour lamp. What would the red lamp disclose? A mouse in a corner playing with an ivory tooth, a little vampire winking at his shoulder, a bed of spiders with a long woman in it.

Suddenly would the beautiful Mrs. Owen be a skeleton with a worm inside her? Oh, oh, God's wrath on such small deer, and the dogs as big as your thumb. Mr. Owen turned up the wick.

And secretly holding hands in the hour between the seconds, in the life that has no time for time, outside under the dark walked Mr. Rafe and the ghost Davies. Was the grass dead under the night, and did the spirit of the grass, greener than Niagara's devil, sprout through the black weather like the flowers through a coffin's cracks? Nothing that was not half the figure of a ghost moved up the miles. And, as the minister had seen his buried squires spin from the system of the dead and, ruddier-cheeked than ever, dance on the orbit of a flower in the last, long acre of Llareggub, so now he saw the buried grass shoot through the new night and move on the hill wind. Were the faces of the west stars the backs of the east? he questioned his dead parishioners. God's wrath, cried Mr. Rafe, in the

shadow of a voice, nothing that was not half the substance of a
man writhing in his shadow as it fell aslant on the hill, on the
double-thumbed piksies about me. Down, down—he slashed at
the blades—down, you bald girls from Merthyr. He slashed at
a walking echo, Ah, ah, oh, ah, cried the voice of Jerusalem,
and Mary, from the moon's arc over the hill, ran like a wolf at
the wailing ministers.

Midnight, guessed Mrs. Owen. The hours had gone by in a
wind.

Mr. Stipe put out his right foot, and nagged at the water with
his left. He crept with ghost Davies through a narrow world; in
his hair were the droppings of birds from the boughs of the mean
trees; leading the ghost through dark dingles, he sprung the
spiked bushes back, and pissed against the wind. He hissed at
the thirsty dead who bit their lips, and gave them a dry cherry;
he whistled through his fingers, and up rose Lazarus like a
weazel. And when the virgin came on a white ass by his grave,
he raised a ragged hand and tickled the ass's belly till it brayed
and threw Mary among the corpse-eaters and the quarrelling
crows.

Mr. Lucytre was not aware of this.

The world, for him, rocked on a snapped foot; the shattered
and the razor-bedded sea, the green skewered hulk with a
stuffing of eyes, the red sea socket itself and the dead ships
crawling around the rim, ached through the gristles and the
bone, the bitten patch, the scaled and bubbling menses, the
elastic issues of the deep, the barbed, stained, and scissored, the
clotted-with-mucus, sawn and thorny flesh, ached on a never-
ending ache. As on a crucifix, and turning on her nails, the
skinny earth, each country pricked to the bladder, each racked
sea torn in the ride, hung despairing in a limp space. What
should the cruel Lucytre, who drags ghost Davies over a timeless
agony, smooth on her wounds? Rust and salt and vinegar and
alcohol, the juice of the upas tree, the scorpion's ointment and a
sponge soaked in dropsy.

The Holy Six stood up.

They took the six glasses of milk from Mr. Owen's tray.

And will the holy gentlemen honour us for the night?

A life in Mrs. Owen was stirring behind the comfortable little
wall. She smiled at Mr. Davies, this time with an intimate

wrinkling of the corners of her mouth; Mr. Owen smiled over his shoulder; and, caught between two smiles and understanding neither, he felt his own lips curl. They shared a mysterious smile, and the Six stood silently behind them.

My child, said Mrs. Owen from her corner, shall be greater than all great men.

Your child is my child, said Mr. Owen.

And Mr. Davies, as suddenly as in the first bewilderment he had gone down upon his knees to pray, leant forward and patted the woman's hand. He would have laid his hands upon the fold of her frock from hip to hip, blessing the unborn under the cotton shroud, but the fear of the power of her eyes held his hand.

Your child is my child, said Mr. Davies.

The ghost in him had coupled with the virgin, the virgin ghost that all the great stirrings of her husband's love had left as whole as a flower in a cup of milk.

But Mr. Owen burst out laughing; he threw back his head, and laughed at the matting shadows, at the oil in the clear, glass bag of the lamp. That there could be seed, shuffling to the spring of heat, in the old man's glands. That there could be life in the ancient loins. Father of the jawbones of asses and the hair-thighed camel's fleas, Mr. Davies swayed before him in a mist of laughter. He could blow the old man up the sky with a puff of his lungs.

He is your child, said Mrs. Owen.

She smiled at the shadow between them, the eunuch shadow of a man that fitted between the curving of their shoulders.

So Mr. Davies smiled again, knowing the shadow to be his. And Mr. Owen, caring for no shadow but that cast on his veins by the rising and the setting of the blood, smiled at them both.

The holy gentlemen would honour them that night.

And the Six circled the three.

PROLOGUE TO AN ADVENTURE

From *Wales*, no. 1 (Summer 1937), pp. 1–6.

As I walked through the wilderness of this world, as I walked through the wilderness, as I walked through the city with the loud electric faces and the crowded petrols of the wind dazzling and drowning me that winter night before the West died, I remembered the winds of the high, white world that bore me and the faces of a noiseless million in the busyhood of heaven staring on the afterbirth. They who nudged through the literate light of the city, shouldered and elbowed me, catching my trilby with the spokes of their umbrellas, who offered me matches and music, made me out of their men's eyes into a manshape walking. But take away, I told them silently, the flannel and cotton, the cheap felt and leather, I am the nakedest and baldest nothing between the pinnacle and the base, an alderman of ghosts holding to watch-chain and wallet on the wet pavement, the narrator of echoes moving in man's time. I have Old Moore by the beard, and the news of the world is no world's news, the gossips of heaven and the fallen rumours are enough and too much for a shadow that casts no shadow, I said to the blind beggars and the paperboys who shouted into the rain. They who were hurrying by me on the narrow errands of the world, time bound to their wrists or blinded in their pockets, who consulted the time strapped to a holy tower, and dodged between bonnets and wheels, heard in my fellow's footsteps the timeless accents of another walking. On the brilliant pavements under a smoky moon, their man's world turning to the bass roll of the traffic, they saw in the shape of my fellow another staring under the pale lids, and heard the spheres turn as he spoke. This is a strange city, gentlemen on your own, gentlemen arm-in-arm making a rehearsed salute, gentlemen with ladies, ladies this is a strange city. For them in the friendless houses in the streets of pennies and pleasures a million ladies and gentlemen moved up in bed, time moved with the practised moon over a million roofs that night, and grim policemen stood at each corner in the black wind. O mister lonely, said the ladies on their own, we shall be naked as new-born mice, loving you long in the short sparks of the night. We are not the ladies with feathers between their breasts, who lay eggs on the quilt. As I walked through the skyscraping centre, where the lamps walked at my side like volted men or the trees of a new scripture, I jostled the devil at my elbow, but lust in his city shadows dogged me under the arches, down the black blind streets. Now in the shape of a bald girl smiling, a wailing wanton with handcuffs for earings, or the lean girls that lived on pickings, now in ragged woman with a muckrake curtseying in the slime, the tempter of angels whispered over my shoulder, We shall be naked but for garters and black stockings, loving you long on a bed of straw-berries and cream, and the nakeder for a ribbon that hides the nipples. We are not the ladies that eat into the brain behind the ear, or feed on the fat of the heart. I remembered the sexless shining women in the first hours of the world that bore me, and the golden sexless men that cried All Praise in the sounds of shape. Taking strength from a sudden shining, I have Old Scratch by the beard, I cried aloud. But the short-time shapes still followed, and the counsellor of an unholy nakedness nagged at my heels. No, not for nothing did the packed thoroughfares confront me at each cross and pavement's turning with these figures in the shapes of sounds, the lamp-chalked silhouettes and the walking frames of dreams, out of a darker allegory than the fictions of the earth could turn in twelve suns' time. There was more than man's meaning to the man-skulled bogies thumbing the skeletons of their noses, to the marrow-merry andrews scratching their armpits in a tavern light, and to the dead man, smiling through his bandages, who laid hand on my sleeve, saying in no man's voice, There is more than man's meaning in a stuffed man talking, split from navel to arsehole, and more in the horned ladies at your heels than a pinch of the cloven delights and the tang of sulphur. Heaven and hell shift up and down the city. I have the God of Israel in the image of a painted boy, and Lucifer, in a woman's shirt, pisses from a win-dow in Damaroid Alley. See now, you shining ones, how the tuner of harps has fallen, and the painter of winds like a bag of henna into the gutter. The high hopes lie broken with broken bottles and suspender-belts, the white mud falls like feathers, there out of Pessary Court comes the Bishop of Bumdom, dressed like a ratcatcher, a holy sister in Gamarouche Mews sharpens her index tooth on a bloodstone, two weazels couple on All Paul's altar. It was an ungodly meaning, or the purpose of the fallen gods whose haloes magnified the wrong-cross-steepled horns on the pointed heads, that windily informed me of man's lower walking, and, as I thrust the dead-and-bandaged and a split-like-cabbage enemy to my right side, up sidled my no-bigger-than-a-thimble friends to the naked left. He who played the sorcerer, appearing all at one time in a dozen sulphurous beckonings, saying, out of a dozen mouths, We shall be naked as the slant-thighed queens of Asia in your dreams, was a symbol in the story of man's journey through the sym-boled city. And that which shifted with the greased lightning of a serpent from the nest holes in the bases of the cathedral pillars, tracking round the margins of the four cindery winds, was, too, a symbol in that city journey. In a mousetailed woman and a holy snake, the symbols of the city writhed before me. But by one red horn I had that double image, tore off the furry stays and leather jacket. We shall be naked, said Old Scratch variously emerging, as a Jewgirl crucified to the bedposts. We are all metaphors of the sound of shape of the shape of sound, break us we take another shape. Sideways the snake and the woman stroked a cross in the air. I saw the starfall that broke a cloud up, and dodged between bonnets and wheels to the iller-lit streets where I saw Daniel Dom lurching after a painted shadow.

We walked into the Seven Sins. Two little girls danced bare-foot in the sawdust, and a bottle splintered on their legs. A negress loosened the straps of her yellow frock and bared a breast, holding a plate under the black flesh. Buy a pound, she said, and thrust her breast in Daniel's face. He faced the women as they moved, a yellow, noisy sea towards us, and caught the half-naked negress by the wrist. Like a woman confronted by a tower, You are so strong, my love, she said, and kissed him full on the mouth. But before the sea could circle us, we were out through the swing-doors into the street and the mid-winter night where the moonlight, salt white no longer, hung wind-lessly over the city. They were night's enemies who made a lamp out of the devil's eye, but we followed a midnight radiance around the corners, like two weird brothers trod in the glittering webprints. In their damp hats and raincoats, in the blaze of shopwindows, the people jostled against us on the pavements, and a gutterboy caught me by the sleeve. Buy an almanac, he said. It was the bitter end of the year. Now the starfall had ended, the sky was a hole in space. How long, how long, lord of the hail, shall my city rock on, and the seven deadly seas wait tidelessly for the moon, the bitter end the last tide-spinning of the full circle. Daniel lamented, trailing the midnight radiance to the door of the Deadly Virtue where the light went out and the seven webprints faded. We were forever climbing the steps of a sea-tower, crying aloud from the turret that we might warn us, as we clambered, of the rusty rack and the spiked maiden in the turret corners. Make way for Mister Dom and friend. Walking into the Deadly Virtue, we heard our names announced through the loudspeaker trumpet of the wooden image over the central mirror, and, staring in the glass as the oracle continued, we saw two distorted faces grinning through the smoke. Make way, said the loudspeaker, for Daniel, ace of Destruction, old Dom the toper of Doom's kitchen, and for the alderman of ghosts. Is the translator of man's manuscript, his walking chapters, said the trumpet-faced, a member of my Deadly Virtue? What is the colour of the narrator's blood? Put a leech on his forearm. Make way, the image cried, for bald and naked Mister Dreamer of the bluest veins this side of the blood-coloured sea. As the sea of faces parted, the bare-backed ladies scraped back from the counter, and the matchstick-waisted men, the trussed and corsetted stilt-walkers with the tits of ladies, sought out the darker recesses of the saloon, we stumbled forward to the fiery bottles. Brandy for the dreamer and the pilgrim, said the wooden voice. Gentlemen, it is my call, said the live loudspeaker, death on my house. It was then, in the tangled hours of a new morning, surrounded by the dead faces of the drinkers, the wail of lost voices, and the words of the one electric image, that Daniel, hair-on-end, lamented first to me of the death on the city and the lost hero of the heart. There can be no armistice for the sexless, golden singers and the sul-

phurous hermaphrodites, the flying beast and the walking bird
that war about us, for the horn and the wing. I could light the
voices of the fiery virgins winking in my glass, catch the brandy-
brown beast and bird as they fumed before my eyes, and kiss the
two-antlered angel. No, not for nothing were these two intangible brandymaids neighbouring Daniel who cried, syringe
in hand, Open your coke-white legs, you ladies of needles,
Dom thunder Daniel is the lightning drug and the doctor.

Now a wind sprang through the room from the dead street;
from the racked tower where two men lay in chains and a hole
broke in the wall, we heard our own cries travel through the
fumes of brandy and the loudspeaker's music; we pawed, in our
tower agony, at the club shapes dancing, at the black girls
tattooed from shoulder to nipple with a white dancing shape,
frocked with snail-headed rushes and capped like antlers. But
they slipped from us into the rubber corners where their black
lovers waited invisibly; and the music grew louder until the
tower cry was lost among it; and again Daniel lurched after a
painted shadow that led him, threading through smoke and
dancers, to the stained window.

Beneath him lay the city sleeping, curled in its streets and
houses, lamped by its own red-waxed and iron stars, with a
built moon above it, and the spires crossed over the bed. I
stared down, rocking at his side, on to the unsmoking roofs and
the burned-out candles. Destruction slept. Slowly the room
behind us flowed, like four waters, down the seven gutters of the
city into a black sea. A wave, catching the live loudspeaker in
its mouth, sucked up the wood and music; for the last time a
mountainous wave circled the drinkers and dragged them
down, out of the world of light, to a crawling sea-bed; we saw
a wave jumping and the last bright eyes go under, the last raw
head, cut like a straw, fall crying through the destroying water.
Daniel and I stood alone in the city. The sea of destruction
lapped around our feet. We saw the starfall that broke the night
up. The glass lights on iron went out, and the waves grew down
into the pavements.

AN ADVENTURE FROM A WORK IN PROGRESS

From *Seven*, no. 4 (Spring 1939), pp. 45–8.

The boat tugged its anchor, and the anchor flew up from the seabed like an iron arrow and hung poised in a new wind and pointed over the corskscrew channels of the sea to the dark holes and caves in the horizon. He saw birds searing out of the pitted distance blind by his anchor as he swam with a seal at his side to the boat that stamped the water. He gripped on the bows like a mane, the arrowing anchor shot north, and the boat sped beneath it with winds and invisible fire puffing and licking. His animal boat split the water into a thousand boatsized seas, bit deep into the flying shoals, halved and multiplied the flying fishes, it dived under waves like a wooden dolphin and wagged the fingering wrack off its stern, it swerved past a black and gold buoy with cathedral chimes and kept cold north. Spray turned to ice as it whipped through his hair, and pierced his cheeks and eyelids, and the running blood froze hard. He saw through a coat of red ice that the sea was transparent; under his boat the drowned dead burned in a pale green, grass-high fire; the sea rained on the flames. But on through the north, between glass hills on which shebears climbed and saw themselves reflected, eating the sea between the paddling floes, a shell of lightning fibres skimming and darting under an anchorbolt, tossed and magnified among the frozen window weeds, through a slow snow-storm whose flakes fell like hills one at a time down the white air, lost in a round sudden house of the six year night and slipping through an arch of sleeping birds each roosted on an icicle, the boat came into blue water. Birds with blue feathers set alight by the sun, with live flames for their crests, flew by the hovering anchor to the trees and bushes on the rims of soft sand round the sea that brushed his boat slowly

and whispered it like a name in letters of parting water towards
a harbour grove and a slowly spinning island with lizards in its
lap. The salmon of the still sail turned to the blue of the birds'
eggs in the tips of the fringing forest of each wave. The feathers
crackled from the birds and drifted down and fell upon bare
rods and stalks that fenced the island entrance, the rods and
stalks grew into trees with musical leaves still burning. The
history of the boat was spelt in knocking water on the hanging
harbour bank; each syllable of his adventure struck on grass
and stone and rang out in the passages of the disturbed rock-
plants and was chattered from flame to tree. The anchor dived
to rest. He strode through the blazing fence. The print of the
ice was melting. The island spun. He saw between trees a tall
woman standing on the opposite bank. He ran directly towards
her but the green thighs closed. He ran on the rim towards her
but she was still the same distance from him on the roundabout
island. Time was about to fall; it had slept without sound under
and over the blaze and spinning; now it was raised ready.
Flowers in the centre of the island caught its tears in a cup. It
hardened and shouted and shone in dead echoes and pearls. It
fell as he ran on the outer rim, and oaks were felled in the acorn
and lizards laid in the shell. He held the woman drowning in
his arms, her driftwood limbs, her winking ballast head of glass;
he fought with her blood like a man with a waterfall turning to
fishdust and ash, and her salvaged seaweed hair twisted
blindly about his eyes. The boat with anchor hovering and
finned oars trembling for water after land, the beaks at the
stern gabbling and the shells alive, was blown alongside him,
by a wind that took a corner on one breath, from the harbour
bank where roots of trees drove up the sky and foliage in
cinders smouldered down, the lopped leg of a bird scratched
against rock, a thundering cave sat upright and bolted mouth-
down into the sea; he dipped the gills of the oars, the cedar-
mast shook like a cloth, warm north the boat sped off again
from an island no longer spinning but split into vanishing caves
and contrary trees. Time that had fallen rested in the edges of its
knives and the hammock of its fires, the memory of the woman
was strong on his hands, her claws and anemones, weedwrack
and urchin hair, the sea was deserted and colourless, direction
was dead as the island and north was a circle, a bird above the

anchor spurted through a stationary cloud to catch its cry, the boat with gilled oars swimming ploughed through the foam in the wake, her pale brow glistened in the new moon of his nails and the drenched thread of her nerves sprang up and down behind them, the stern beaks quacked and yawned, crabs clacked from the shells, a mist rose up that dressed and un-shaped the sky and the sea flowed in secret. Through the mist, dragging a black weather with it, a spade-shaped shoal of clouds tacked to its peak, a broken moon, a wind with trumpets, came a mountain in a moment. The boat struck rock. The beaks were still. The shells snapped shut. He leaped into mud as the wind cried his name to the flapping shoals; his name rolled down the mountain, echoed through caves and crevices, ducked in venomous pools, slap on black walls, translated into the voice of dying stone, growling through slime into silence. He gazed at the mountain peak; a cloud obscured it, cords of light from the moon were looped around the tentacles of the crags. Lightning with a horn and bone on, with gristle white as a spine hardening and halving the forked sides, struck through the tacked cloud cap, lit the stone head, scorched the mist-curled fringe, cut through the cords until the moon sailed upwards like a kite. With the turning out of the lightning, the jackknife doubling up of the limp spine, the weather in tow rocked to work and flight in a sealed air, the mountain vanished leaving a hole in space to keep the shape of his horror as he sank, as the monuments of the dark mud toppled and his raised arms were cemented against rock with the wet maggot sacks and the mixed, crawling breasts of statues and creatures who once stood on the ledges of the mountain foot or blocked the crying mouths of caves. The wind, blowing matter with a noise, stuck to his cheek. The sea climbed his limbs like a sailor. Bound and drowning in that dismembered masonry, his eyes on a level with the shuffled circle of headpieces floating, he saw the light-ning dart to strike again, and the horned bone stiffen among the forks; hope, like another muscle, broke the embraces of the nuzzling bodies, thrust off the face that death-masked his, for the mountain appeared on the strike of light and the hollow shape of his horror was filled with crags and turrets, rock webs and dens, spinning black balconies, the loud packed smashing of separate seas, and the abominable substances of a new colour.

The world happened at once. There was the furnished mountain built in a flash and thunderclap colliding. The shapes of
rain falling made a new noise and number. And the lightning
stayed striking; its charted shaft of sawteeth struck and bit in
continual light; one blind flash was a year of mornings. The
mummyfolds, the mudpots, the wet masks, the quick casts, the
closing sheathes, melted under the frostbite heat of that unwink-
ing lightning. He boxed free from the statues and the caved and
toppling watchers. From a man-sized dent in a melting thigh he
came up strung with shells and mussed with weed like a child
from the roots of the original sea into a dazzling bed. Once on
hard land, with shells that swung from his hair ringing from the
tail of a weed, and shells repeating the sea, he shook away
calamity, bounced the weeds off his bare breast, threw back his
head until the pealing shells took in their echo the voices of all
miscellaneous water, and grappled with the mountainside. His
shadow led and beckoned; he turned curves of the eel-backed
paths, his shadow pointed to the footprints that appeared before
his feet; he followed where his footprints led, saw the smudged
outline of his hand on a wet stone as he quarrelled with stones
and trees towards it up an attacking valley; animals closed
their lips round the shout of a wind walking by and scooped his
name to welcome it up hollow trunks and walls. He followed
the flight of his name: it slipped to a stop at the peak: there a
tall woman caught the flying name to her lips. He flourished in
the middle of the pain of the mountain and joy sped with his
shadow, the strong memory of the driftwrack woman was dead
on his hands digging deep in the soil towards this stranger tall
as a pulled tree and whiter at that great shortening distance
than the lightning-coloured sea a hundred dangers below. The
thighs smooth as groundstone and sensual cleft, limpet eye and
musselmouth, the white boulders bent, blue shadows and
pricked berries, the torrential flowers and blacks of the bush on
the skull and the muffed pits, the draped cellars, the lashed
stones, the creased face on the knees, all for a moment while he
stood in love were still and near. Then slowly her peak in a
cloud's alcove—carved animals on an abbey, wind in an amice,
arching accusing her—rose with his lovely dashing from stillness. Slowly her peak got up the cloudy arches, the stones he
stumbled on followed her at the same speed. Though he hugged

like a bear and climbed fast, she kept her distance from him. The mountain in the intervals of his breathing grew many times its size until time fell and cut and burned it down. The peak collapsed, the mountain folded, he clasped the woman diminishing in his arms; the downpours of her hair were short falls, her limbs stunted, her hands blunt, her teeth were small and square as dice and the rot marked them. A halo cracked like china, wings were spoked. Blood flapped behind all the windows of the world. And with the wasting of her limbs suddenly she grew young. Holding her small body, he cried in the nightmare of a naked child kissing and blaspheming close, breasts small as pears with milk foaming from them, the innocent holes of the open eyes, the thin, rouged musselmouth, when the head falls, the eyes loll, the small throat snaps, and the headless child lies loving in the dark. The mad bug trotted in at the ear with the whole earth on a feeler. With his cries she caved in younger. He held her hard. The marrow in her bones was soft as syrup. From a scar in the peak came a shadow with black gamp and scarlet basin. She dangled there with bald and monstrous skull, bunched monkey face and soaked abdominal tail. Out of the webbed sea-pig and water-nudging fish a white pool spat in his palm. Reeling to run seaward and away, he trod the flats of waves. The splintered claw of a crab struck from the killed hindershells. And, after the anchor burrowing through blind cloud, he rowed and sailed, that the world might happen to him once, past the events of revolving islands and elastic hills, on the common sea.

THE DEATH OF THE KING'S CANARY

Excerpts from the unpublished typescript in the keeping of the poet's
Literary Executors, David Higham Associates Ltd. This satirical
novel was written in collaboration with the late John Davenport. It
had, however, originally been conceived as a radio play in collaboration with Charles Fisher, titled 'The Murder of the King's
Canary' (a title originally suggested by Pamela Hansford Johnson).
In March 1938 Thomas wrote to Charles Fisher suggesting that they
might turn it into a novel. Work was begun on it in that year, but
abandoned. In the summer of 1940, Thomas started a new collaboration on the novel with John Davenport, while he and Caitlin
Thomas were staying with Mr and Mrs Davenport in their manor
house near Marshfield in Gloucestershire. The novel, as Thomas
described it in a letter to Vernon Watkins, is 'a fantastic thriller'.
Conceived in a spirit of fun, it concerns the nomination of a new
Poet Laureate (the 'Canary'). The bulk of the action, with grotesque
'thriller' devices, take place in a large country house where prominent English poets (thinly disguised) are in residence, along with a
circus company camped in the grounds. Because of the satire on
actual poets, the work is considered libellous, and thus cannot as yet
be published *in toto*. In this selection, some of the writers are on their
way to the country house.

The Admiral Nelson, a decrepit rowing boat nearly half full of
water, bobbed on the choppy sea, a mile or two off the Cardigan
coast. Two young men in high sea boots, corduroy trousers, and
open cricket shirts, sat contentedly on either side of the boat,
and fished for flats. A small keg of Irish whiskey floated in the
water in the boat; and every few minutes, and sometimes more
often, one of the two fishermen would bend down, silently, and
lift the keg up. This regular motion shook the Admiral Nelson
like a great wave.

The two fishermen clung on to the keg for their lives.

'My turn for the big swig,' said Tom Agard. Because it was

highly dangerous to drink from a barrel while standing knee-deep in water in a pitching boat that might at any moment turn right over or go straight down like a stone, it had been arranged that they should take it in turns to have a long drink and that the man whose turn it was for a quick gulp should hold the barrel.

Tom Agard drank deep. The whiskey went glugging down into his whale-like belly. Little Owen Tudor held the big barrel against his chest. Tom Agard was kneeling in the water. A wave came over the side, and Owen thought of death.

'My gulp now,' he said. Agard's ponderous rising was the most dangerous moment of all. 'Oh, oh, Jesu. She's tossing like a horse. We're done for this time. Over we go. Great green death. Sharks and waterdogs. Old men of the sea. Davy Jones, Davy Jones, catch me, I'm coming.' The staggering exchanging of the barrel, the little swallow, the dignified whiskey lurch, then again the barrel dropped like a thunderbolt into water.

'It is, in some ways, a remarkably encouraging appointment,' Tom Agard said, leaning back at his ease and addressing the whole attentive sea. 'To appoint a man whose work is a studied insult to all academic balderdash: it's a charming conceit.'

He belched comfortably. He weighed between 19 and 20 stone and had a reddish beard. He looked jovial and Fal-staffian, and could be so on occasion; but his mind was more precise than Rabelaisian. Owen Tudor had a thin precise look, dark and subtle, more like a French than an English poet, and more critic than poet, at that. This, too, was misleading. Strangers would find themselves involved in Elizabethan situations, which usually ended very uncomfortably for them and very amusingly for Owen. You would start the day drinking enormously with Tom, and find yourself at the end of it listening to a lucid criticism of the works of Webern; whereas a day with Owen beginning with an analysis of Unamuno would very likely end in the bear pit at Whipsnade or in an aeroplane flying to an unknown destination. Obviously enough, when they were together, like the Chinese meta-physicians, they 'combined their information,' as it were, and felt in harmony.

'Where is that ham, you gross buffoon?'

'My dear little friend, you are sitting on it. Get up and we will eat.'

When they had baled out the results of this manœuvre, Owen continued, his face full of ham and pickles.

'A charming conceit—oh yes. I'm not complaining about the appointment.'

'No, indeed, but it's a pretty puzzle. I was up with Byrd. I remember throwing him into Trinity fountain. He bore no malice; and I made settings for those early parodies of his. You remember the music was parody, too. The Ravel one was rather good as I remember. But not a nice man.'

'You're a puritan. Mine for the big swig.'

The proof pages of Owen's new poems were severely damaged.

'Never mind. Give the printer something to think about.'

'Why does one never catch anything? It's pleasant here but why don't we sit at home?'

He looked flatly at the tall Georgian house barely visible across the bay.

'We seem to be a long way from things. Let's row back. I'll steer.'

'You will not, you triple-bellied drunkard.'

'Very well. Very well. Where are the oars?'

There were no oars. Owen began to speak.

'Tut tut!' said Tom. 'You waste breath. It's an omen. We shall catch something. And we can continue our discussion in peace. Mine for the big swig.'

*   *   *   *   *   *

It wasn't a very comfortable car. Not so bad for Tom Agard, who drove it; hellish for Owen Tudor, crushed between buttocks and gear-levers. The car went fairly fast but became white hot; and the smell of petrol was sickening. But it was a puncture that stopped them first. There was a long gravelly skid and a lurch. The car settled on one side, a sinking ship.

'Foundered.'

'Whose turn to change the wheel?'

'Don't prevaricate. Just get on with it.'

Agard extricated himself from behind the wheel with the laborious precision of a circus elephant.

Tudor sat back, moderately comfortable for the first time that day, smirking. He whistled a little tune, lit a cigarette and uncorked a bottle of Audit. Agard regarded this performance gloomily. Tudor affected to be unaware of the two great pouchy eyes. The fat man got out the jack with a lot of unnecessary noise, and fell in the dusty road with a groan. Tudor whistled a hymn tune, double time, with intervals for refreshment.

'Would you be so good as not to whistle?'

'What, not finished yet?'

'Just a drink and a cigarette . . .'

'Not a bit of it. We're late as it is. Look lively.'

An open brewer's lorry roared by. Tudor was saved from physical violence. Agard's rage was diverted. He shouted imprecations after the lorry, his mouth filled with dust, then bent once more to his task.

Roger Rashleigh's enormous cigar fitted with the Duisenberg he drove, but he was out of scale with both. A very small millionaire. He drove easily and well at ninety miles an hour. Pity one couldn't drive fast in England. In Europe or America, driving Marxist friends from one Conference to another, one could really move. He cornered smoothly and passed the crazy, pile-up car.

Agard had abandoned the use of the jack and was holding up the machine by the back axle, while he bawled for help. Rashleigh recognized the swollen face of the musician, and reversed. Tudor had not moved. Agard released his hold and the car relapsed once more.

'Hello, Tom,' said Roger. 'In difficulties?'

Agard advanced with a menacing buffalo's tread.

'Can I give you a lift?'

In an instant Tudor was out of the seat and scrabbling for more Audit; Agard sat down on the running board; Roger walked round his great car, invisible, and joined them.

'Going to Dymmock, I suppose? There's going to be quite a party. We can all go together.'

They got into the car.

*   *   *   *   *   *

The berwer's lorry—Halifax's Golden Prize Beer is Full of Good Cheer—which was shaking along in the direction of Dymmock's Hall contained six men of letters. They sat on cases of Halifax in the open back of the lorry. Sidney Gorman, the Australian historian, had tampered with each case in turn, but had not managed to get one open. The cases were scratched, kicked, splintered. Gorman had broken two penknives and cut his thumbs.

Ostler waved his deerstalker at the broken down car. 'Two poets,' he said. That seemed to explain everything.

'Tudor doesn't make sense. He drinks,' said Mallow.

'Dear God above me,' said O'Brien, 'there's only one poet among the whole lot of you and he isn't here. He's the man who wrote *that* little poem.' He pointed to the Halifax slogan painted unsteadily on the back of the driver's cabin: Halifax's was a small dishonest concern whose products even Sidney Gorman had been heard to refer to as 'No bloody good—o,' after drinking a gallon in bed.

'There isn't a breath of poetry in it at all,' MacManus shouted. He was hot and tired and covered with dust; the motion of the lorry upset his stomach; last night he had given a lecture on Burns to the empty chairs in his bedsitting room, and bottle imps inside the cupboard had clapped and cheered. Life was catching him up again. 'It's doggerel, doggerel,' he shouted. He told them what poetry was. He gave them examples.

'We'll burrn the broot and fadge our coot
By Whalsey's mimring whutter,'

he recited, 'that's the real stuff.'

'What's whutter?' Gorman asked. He did not care if anyone answered him or not. His cuts were smarting. He had no idea where he was going. Without any hope of success, he struck at a case marked 'Special Golden' with Ostler's ornate walking stick.

Mahaffey said, from his corner: 'Why don't you burn the box?' He was able to make every question he asked sinister and sly. It was one of his most engaging tricks, and had lost him more friends than he had ever needed. Halifax's unbreakable case of repellent ale became, through his twinkling leer, his nods and shudders of contented malice, a symbol of English corruption, a secret meeting place of reactionary M.P.'s, a trove of Montague Normans. 'I've got a big box of matches,' he said. He brought them out of his pocket, slowly.

Gorman, trembling, lit a match and put it against the side of the case. The match went out immediately. He lit another.

'No, no. Use your head, man,' said Ostler. 'Proper way is to soak the box in paraffin.' He made no effort to move. It was enough to know.

'Who's got any paraffin?'

The lorry rattled on. Those are trees over there, thought Mallow. Oak trees, perhaps. That was hay; or was it corn? which was the yellowest?

The lorry passed the barley field at a great speed.

Mallow, a nature poet with a considerable London reputation, was always bewildered by the country: the common properties of his verse grew unrecognizably alive around him. In the distance, a real ploughman with a white horse moved through a field of something or other, contradicting every line of 'Country Sonnets: A Sheaf' and 'The Soul and the Flower' (5th. thousand). The country was against him. 'Apples,' that rhymed with 'dapples,' were big red threats on a tree. He had never realised that the lyrical hedgerow was so tall and tangled and dark. In Theobald's Road these things took on a safe perspective. He began to long for the 'Angel and Crown.' The bar would be crowded, celebrities falling like skittles.

The others looked uncertainly around them. There didn't seem to be any paraffin.

Rashleigh's great car rocketted past them.

'Three poets now,' said Ostler. He liked order.

'I remember,' O'Brien said, 'when I was a nipper in Sligo me old man and mself burnt down Lady Rafferty's barn. We wanted to know what she'd say. We took the door off its hinges and soaked it in petrol and the old one stole a blowlamp. In just under an hour, by Jesus, there was a fire like Hell itself and the Lady came caterwauling out. The cursing, the cursing,' he said happily. 'She hit the old fool down with her shoe, and her foot was big as a boat, and then she had me larruped and the whole blessed afternoon cost me daddy the price of three pigs.'

'Stop the lorry,' said Mahaffey.

Ostler beat on the window. The driver pulled up. She was Mrs. Burgin, the landlady of the Bells, a small, Halifax-tied house on the outskirts of London. An invaluable woman and very experienced.

'Mrs Burgin,' said Mahaffey, 'will you kindly suck out a drop of petrol from the tank for us? We want to make a little fire in the back.'

Mrs. Burgin tossed her red hair. 'Suck it yourself, big boy,' she said.

The six men conferred in whispers.

'Twist her arm,' Gorman suggested. The others turned on him at once.

'Australian pig.'

'It's a dirty torturer you'd make yourself all for a bottle of muck,' said MacManus.

'We'll have to suck it in turns,' Mahaffey said. 'You begin, Mallow.'

'What shall we put it in?'

'Doesn't Mallow wear boots?' said Mahaffey.

Gorman said, 'Give her The Key.'

They made Mallow remove one boot, but could not make him give the other up. 'That's a real friend!' said Mahaffey. They called Mallow an Englishman, and climbed out of the lorry.

After several preliminary cursings and spittings, Mallow managed to catch quite a lot of petrol in his mouth. 'Hold it!' MacManus shouted. 'Don't try to say anything! Who's taken the boot?'

When they had filled the boot and had seen to Mallow, calming him with promises of the first bottle, they climbed back and poured the petrol over the Halifax case. Mrs. Burgin drove on.

Soon there was a roaring little fire. The straw on the floor of the lorry caught with a blaze. Shouting and jostling, the six writers kept jumping away from the flames and encouraging each other to take off his coat and put the fire out. In this confusion they drove into Dymmock courtyard.

The courtyard was full of people running. Mrs. Burgin, taking no risk of an accident, guided the lorry expertly into the pond.

BETTY LONDON

Alternative title 'Suffer Little Children'.

Excerpt from the manuscript-and-typescript version in the Lockwood Memorial Library, written in 1945. This feature-film script
was written when the poet was working for Donald Taylor's
company, Strand Films, which was the most active at the time in
making serious documentary films for the Ministry of Information.
Thomas had begun work in films in September 1940. This particular script was in fact bought by Gainsborough Pictures Ltd, but
was never actually made into a film. Some of the material was,
however, used in another film called 'Good Time Girl', featuring
Diana Dors. Though on the whole this film script is not such a
success as Thomas's other work in this medium, this particular
excerpt illustrates how such work prepared Thomas for the comic
mode of *Under Milk Wood*. The script deals with a young delin-
quent's life in a reform school. In this excerpt, she has been placed
as a maid in a guest-house.

The Steamy Basement Kitchen of Mrs. Foster's Boarding
House.

It is a big, dark, overcrowded, stone floored kitchen, with a very
large range and an old-fashioned bell-indicator over the door:
a kitchen that can have changed in no essential since the more
gloomy basement days of the last century. The cook, a faded,
doleful woman, is making pastry at a table. Betty is busy at a
wash tub, up to the elbows in suds. Betty wears a long stiff
white dress, white cap, big apron. We see her close. A bell rings,
loudly. Neither Betty nor the Cook looks up or turns around.

BETTY : I bet it's Mr. Dibdin the author—oh why does he live
so high up . . .

COOK : Perhaps it's Mr. Chatterjee.

And Betty begins to giggle.

COOK : What'd he call you when you took his tea up?

BETTY: My little passion flower . . .

The bell rings again.

COOK (without turning round, in a high, sad voice): It's only Mrs. Foster again . . . always ringing, like a fireman . . .

Betty turns to look at the bell-indicator. We see the rows of names, and a star coming into place on MRS. FOSTER. Betty sighs, wipes her suddy hands, takes off her wet apron, pats her clothes into place, and goes out. When she is at the door, the Cook calls out after her in a doleful voice:

COOK: Look out for Mr. Chatterjee . . .

CUT TO Betty going up the creaking uncarpeted kitchen stairs. We see only her feet and legs.

CUT TO Betty's feet and legs climbing another, shabby-carpeted, flight of stairs.

CUT TO Mrs. Foster's Bedroom.

It is a large, heavily Victorian room; the curtains are drawn. A figure is sitting up in bed. From the end of the room opposite the door, we see the door open and Betty come in.

BETTY: Good morning, ma'am.

Betty curtsies in the half dark, towards the bed. She crosses to the window, pulls open the heavy curtains. Morning light comes into the room. We see, clearly, the figure sitting up in bed: Mrs. Foster, with a nightcap on. We see the solid, inconvenient furniture, the dark cupboards, the screens, the trinkets of every kind on the laced dressing table, the pictures on the wall of men with beards, women with bosoms, cattle with sunsets. Betty stands, facing Mrs. Foster, in the middle of the room. Mrs. Foster is fat, and has some difficulty in breathing.

MRS. FOSTER: Good morning, Betty. Has Miss Seymour Carr had her Russian tea?

BETTY: Yes'm.

MRS. FOSTER: And Indian tea for Mr. Chatterjee?

BETTY: Yes'm.

MRS. FOSTER: Mr. Dibdin the author?

Betty nods.

MRS. FOSTER: Captain and Mrs. Bottral?

Betty nods.

MRS. FOSTER: Now first I want the stairs dusted from top to bottom—and no pushing the dust under the carpet. And after breakfast you dust the dining room. Other guest houses, I am told, have vacuum cleaners to encourage idleness among the servants. There were no vacuum cleaners in my day. And there were no idle servants! Then, you clean all the rooms on the second and third floors, not forgetting the offices. Then you scrub the front steps *and* the area steps, and then carry on with your washing. Now, there must be no dust and no noise. Dust is an enemy. I am *down* on dust. My mother was down on dust. Dust and noise and Fosters cannot live in the same house. That is all.

BETTY: Yes'm.

She turns to go out.

MRS. FOSTER: Have you forgotten something?

Betty turns again.

BETTY (puzzled): No, mum.

MRS. FOSTER: Think again, Betty . . .

And Betty curtsies.

MRS FOSTER (Graciously): That is correct. We mustn't forget the little civilities that help to turn the wheels around . . .

And Betty goes out.

DISSOLVE TO Betty dusting the stairs.

DISSOLVE TO Miss Seymour Carr's bedroom.

There are some Eastern pictures on the wall, and a few oddments of Chinese furniture. Betty is cleaning the room. From a door off the room, Miss Seymour Carr comes in: a middle-aged lady dressed in the art-nouveau fashion of some years ago: long dress, peasant blouse, fringe, heavy necklace and bracelets.

MISS SEYMOUR CARR (brightly): Poor child! Work work work . . .

She crosses to an Eastern objet d'art—an inlaid thing of little drawers and shelves—and unlocks it.

MISS SEYMOUR CARR: Don't you ever feel you *must* have some colour in your life? Something gay, and . . . strange?

BETTY: Yes, Miss Seymour Carr . . .

MISS SEYMOUR CARR: I know. You are like myself—you are
one of those who *feel*! I *knew* it the first day you came here.
BETTY: Yes, mum.

Miss Seymour Carr takes out a string of garish beads. She
crosses to Betty, holds them for a moment against Betty's
throat.

MISS SEYMOUR CARR: There! You see? But of course you
don't, how silly I am . . . Look in the mirror . . . Yes, take
them for a moment . . .

Betty turns to a mirror, holds the beads against her throat. We
see her in the mirror.

MISS SEYMOUR CARR'S VOICE: I *live* for colour . . . and
shape, of course. There, give it to me.

Betty turns from the mirror. Now we see Miss Seymour Carr
take the beads, put them away.

MISS SEYMOUR CARR: I'd rather part with my right hand . . .

She looks at her right hand.

MISS SEYMOUR CARR: I should have been a pianist . . . Yes
I'd rather part with *anything* than my little treasure trove . . .
Look . . .

Betty looks at the shelves of Miss Seymour Carr's inlaid
treasure-trove.

MISS SEYMOUR CARR: These ear-rings—like blood drops . . .

We see the ring. Miss Seymour Carr takes it out, lifts it up,
shows it to Betty.

That ring was a gift from an admirer. 'Savage beauty to
sav—' well, I mustn't tell you *all* he said. (Looking at Betty
who is looking at the jewellery): You haven't had an admirer
yet, Betty? No, no, how could you, I am *so* silly. I'm always
being told by my friends how *silly* I am—they seem to like it,
for some reason—how could you in that dreadful place . . .

Miss Seymour Carr carefully locks up the cabinet.

Do you ever *read*?
BETTY: I used to read, mum, when I was young . . .
MISS SEYMOUR CARR: 'When I was young!' O my dear
child, you must think of *me* as old as the hills . . . Ah, but then

it was only fairy stories wasn't it? You haven't read any real
love stories?

BETTY: No . . .

Miss Seymour Carr crosses to a desk, takes out a paper backed
book.

MISS SEYMOUR CARR: Then you must start straight away . . .
  Take this, and when you've finished it, you can have another
  . . . I've got *heaps* . . .

Betty takes the book.

  No, don't thank me, don't thank me . . . Take it with you . . .
  They're beginning a new serial in it. . . . You'll get to *love*
  Rex Trent . . .

Betty takes up her mop and dust pan and paper backed book.

DISSOLVE TO Dining Room of Boarding House.

Miss Foster at one end of the table, an elderly man, Mr.
Dibdin at the other: Miss Seymour Carr also, and a few other
nondescript people. Mrs. Foster rises and rings an old-fashioned
bell-pull.

CUT TO Basement Kitchen.

Betty is loading a tray. The Cook is sad at the long range. We
hear the bell ringing.

COOK: Clang, clang, another fire . . .

BETTY: Don't they eat quick . . . And then Mrs. Foster said,
  'Dust's an enemy. I'm down on dust. My *mother* was down on
  dust, too,' she said . . .

COOK: That's where her mother is now alright. . . .

Betty takes the tray out.

CUT TO Betty's feet and legs going upstairs.

CUT TO Betty going into the Dining Room. She puts the tray
down. The plates rattle.

MRS. FOSTER: Quiet, quiet! No noise in the house, please . . .

CUT TO the kitchen.

Betty is scrubbing the floor. The Cook is about the kitchen,
sadly banging at pots and pans. There is quite a lot of noise.

COOK: I'd like her to have my feet . . .

BETTY: Miss Seymour Carr lent me a book, I'll show it to you
  tonight . . .

COOK : I'd like her to have them for one day, that's all. What sort of a book?

BETTY : It's a love story.

COOK : Perhaps Mr. Chatterjee upstairs wrote it. Is it about passion flowers?

BETTY : No, it's about someone called Rex Trent and he's a Captain in the Army . . .

COOK : He wouldn't be if he had my feet . . .

PART II

MODERN POETRY

From *Swansea Grammar School Magazine*, vol. 26, no. 3 (December 1929), pp. 82–4.

To attempt a comprehensive survey of Georgian poetry within a restricted space is to produce almost impassable difficulties. Poetry has never been so wide and varied as it is today, and the individualism of nearly every poet asserts itself to such an extent that no definite poetical schools can be discerned. It is obvious that in dealing generally with this subject, many poets must be either ignored or forgotten. Hardy, Bridges, William Watson, Newbolt, Binyon, Kipling, Noyes, and many other important names cannot even be mentioned, none of them being typical of the modern artistic spirit, and none being strictly Georgian.

The most important element that characterises our poetical modernity is freedom—essential and unlimited—freedom of form, of structure, of imagery and of idea. It had its roots in the obscurity of Gerard Manley Hopkins' lyrics, where, though more often than not common metres were recognised, the language was violated and estranged by the efforts of compressing the already unfamiliar imagery.

The first form of freedom was found in the poetry of Robert Bridges, who introduced free rhythm into the confines of orthodox metre. De la Mare enlarged upon this process of innovation with convention, and at the present time Sacheverell Sitwell presents a great deal of his strange confusion of thought and beauty in the heroic couplet.

The freedom of idea can be found abundantly in any anthology. Assuming that no subject is an unpoetical subject, the neo-Romanticists (headed by T. S. Eliot, and, in the majority of his moments, by James Joyce) give us their succession of sordid details, their damp despondent atmosphere, and their attraction for the gutter, 'the sawdust restaurants with oyster shells,' 'the yellow smoke of streets,' and 'cigarettes in corridors, and cocktail smells in bars.'

But this freedom does not confine itself to the writing of such crudities as would have disgusted our Victorians and our Augustans. At the head of the twilight poets, W. B. Yeats introduces a fragile unsubstantial world, covered with mysticism and mythological shadows. His entire poetical creation is brittle, and his cry,

> I have spread my dreams under your feet,
> Tread softly because you tread on my dreams,

is justified.

Neither is the variety of freedom composed only of vague shadows and bitter crudities. The simplicity of the early poets, Herrick and Lovelace, modernized in subject-matter and treatment, can be found in the best of our present hedgerow poets. W. H. Davies has written some of the most charming poems in the language, the simple beauty of which makes up for the lack of deep thought in most of his other work.

The freedom of imagery can best be exemplified by the small Imagist group, founded by John Gould Fletcher, the American. Richard Aldington, the best known Imagist of today, has adopted the original method of accentuating the image and making it first in importance in the poem, but has modified it and made it more intelligible. Fletcher loaded his work with colour and rich scintillation to such an extent that the real depth of one image was lost, owing to the blinding effect of the next. In such lines as:

> Lacquered mandarin moments, palanquins swaying and
>   balancing,
> Amid the vermilion pavilions, against the jade balustrades.
> Silver, filaments, golden flakes settling downwards,
> Rippling, quivering flutters,
> The rain rustling with the sun,

the glitter is mainly superficial, the rush of innumerably coloured words producing a kaleidoscopic effect that cannot stimulate or satisfy the imagination.

The position of the Sitwells in poetical art is indefinite, only because they are curiously regarded as obscurists, while a closer examination of their work cannot fail to impress the mind with images and thoughts of a new and astonishing clarity. They cannot be considered as a poetic whole. Admittedly, the same philosophic principle governs both Edith's and Osbert's work, but it is only this basic quality which can make their poetry comparable. Building on the same foundations of dramatic lyricism and satire, their structures are entirely different. Edith achieves narrowness of poetical effect within wide psychological and natural fields. Her poems are essentially feminine, with their shrewd grasp of detail, their sudden illuminations, and their intensity of emotion, and it is the more insignificant mannerisms of her femininity that make her poems difficult. Osbert, whose poetry is the least distinguished of the three, is a painter of more definite emotions, lacking the hard colour of Edith and the gradual beauty of Sacheverell. His satire is violent, but the violence carries with it a redeeming conviction. Sacheverell is the most difficult to become intimate with. His difficulty is genuine, the strangeness of the picture he sees and wishes to explain, justifying the strangeness of the image he employs.

It is obvious that when a really revolutionary movement takes place in any art, there must be a justification for it, either material or intellectual. What changed the course of English poetry completely was the Great War, the brutality of which failed to warp man's outlook and ideals, and caused some of the bitterest and the loveliest poetry in the language to be written. Out of the darkness came the clear light of genius: Siegfried Sassoon, with his white-hot satire and beauty; Rupert Brooke, who sacrificed his ardour, his mental and physical sublimity for the country that was never allowed to realise him fully; Robert Nichols, whose wild impetuosity and deep reserve flamed and dwindled with the spirit of his passion; Wilfred Owen, Robert Graves, Julian Grenfell, and the other heroes who built towers of beauty upon the ashes of their lives.

It is the more recent poetry of today that shows the clearest influence of the war. The incoherence caused by anguish and animal horror, and the shrill crudity which is inevitable in poetry produced by such war, are discarded. Instead, we have a more contemplative confusion, a spiritual riot. No poet can find sure ground; he is hunting for it, with the whole earth perturbed and unsettled about him. To-day is a transitional period. D. H. Lawrence, the body-worshipper who fears the soul; Edmund Blunden, who has immersed himself in the English countryside; Richard Church, the poet of detached contemplation; Ezra Pound, the experimental mystic, are only laying the foundations of a new art. The poetry that will be ultimately built upon these foundations, seems, as far as can be conjectured at present, to offer promise of a high and novel achievement.

THE FILMS

From *Swansea Grammar School Magazine*, vol. 27, no. 2 (July 1930), pp. 54–6.

The evolution of the motion-picture from the crude experimentalism of pre-war years to the polished artistry of to-day has taken place during a very short period. It was not until the beginning of the twentieth century that it was possible to present natural things in natural motion on a screen. Today, less than thirty years later, every shade of physical emotion, however slight or subtle, can be shown among natural and often naturally coloured surroundings.

The first picture that could be taken seriously was produced by D. W. Griffith in 1907. He brought a greater sense of balance and artistic understanding to that film than had hitherto been thought of, and introduced the now familiar tricks of the 'close-up' the 'fade out' and the 'cut back'. He realised the importance of motion-pictures, not as freak exhibitions, but as works of art produced through an entirely new medium. The first film that was taken seriously was Adolph Zukor's 'Queen Elizabeth', produced in 1912. Zukor had been for a long time contemplating the introduction of famous stage-stars on to the screen, and he made his first attempt at this by casting Sarah Bernhardt as Elizabeth. The film met with instant appreciation, but, with a few notable exceptions, stage-stars have not been successful on the screen, partly from the more exacting demands of silent presentation and partly because good stage technique does not necessarily mean a good screen technique.

In 1914 D. W. Griffith produced 'The Birth of a Nation'. This was quite easily superior to every other pre-war film. It was devastating in its racial results, causing rioting and some bloodshed, but it proved more than ever to him that motion-pictures were world-wide influences.

87

During the war, the few English studios that had been trying to compete with the many more American ones, were entirely suspended. When English producers turned back to their trade in 1919 they found that America had got complete hold over the world, and dominated every market. It was not until two or three years ago that England woke up to the fact that English producers were bringing forth many very fine films. Up to then the public had been so used to seeing thousands of American pictures and occasional and almost invariably bad English ones, that they did not get to know that there were some really intelligent producers at work in England. Now, the pictures produced in this country are quite as good and nearly as many as those produced in America.

The stories of the early films were simple and obvious, but as time went on and the public became more sophisticated, it was necessary to think of plots that did not always deal with the human triangle, or the hero, the heroine and the villain in a breathless intrigue with an inevitable ending. Consequently the hero became more humanized, and even the heroine had her faults, while the villain was not branded by a cloak and a series of sinister gestures, but was allowed more ordinary dress and movements. Then, as plots wore thinner and thinner, the classics were taken from their shelves, dusted, abridged, renovated by superior intellects, and finally, were represented on the screen with more taste and understanding, until today many of the best films are those based upon, or woven round, famous novels and plays.

Film-acting requires distinct subtlety of action. Spoken words are, as often as possible, eliminated, and visual symbols used instead. That is, nearly the whole effect of a film depends upon the comprehensibility of features, facial expressions, and movements of the body. The early actors, dependent so much upon speech, found themselves at a loss to adapt themselves to the screen. Consequently, their acting was exaggerated and absurd. They magnified every emotion and overstressed every facial expression. They indulged almost invariably in orgies of grief, hysteria, and inarticulate anger. Henry B. Walthall, in 1914, showed that such exaggeration was unnecessary, by giving a new and delicate film performance in 'The Birth of a Nation'. He employed the slightest gestures and the most illuminating innuendoes. His acting was a landmark in the progress of the motion-picture. From his time has come a long line of actors and actresses who have made themselves universally admired for their brilliance and charm.

In the few points I have dealt with, I have made no mention of sound. The coming of the talkies has widened many fields and narrowed many others. There is no way of treating the motion-picture with sound and without sound: they are far too differentiated. Sound-technique is in the same state now as silent technique was when D. W. Griffith evolved his own methods of pictorial representation, adding inestimably to its progress. Whether there will be a Griffith for sound-films is a matter that is best left to time.

Synchronized films up to 1930 have been distinctly disappointing. Crudity was expected, but both American and English producers have taken sound for granted, and have been over-confident of themselves. The older and established producers, especially, have merely added it to their screen-properties, without realising that it is something new which cannot be tackled by any old methods but which requires a special way of approach. Even film-pioneers must start at the beginning of sound-film production, and learn what there is to be learnt.

THE SINCEREST FORM OF FLATTERY
(A Literary Course)

From *Swansea Grammar School Magazine*, vol. 28, no. 2 (July 1931), pp. 191–6.

The true author is bred not born. He who reads, and digests sufficient of the work of his contemporaries, should have no difficulty in writing the sort of things they write, as well as they do, if not even better.

Take the Russian novel. The author need know nothing at all about the Russian language, country or culture. All he needs is the right temperament. Let him study the following incident, which contains most of the necessary ingredients:

The room is cold and dark. One can hear, outside in the snow, the sounds of Grafel, the wagoner, beating his wife monotonously with a bottle. It is cold, cold.

Little Ivanov lifts his head from between his hands. 'Why is it always snowing, uncle Vidna?' he asks, in a voice full of that yearning and that impenetrable grief he cannot yet understand.

Uncle Vidna, combing his beard on to the table, stops.

'It is life, Life, Little Ivanov,' he replies, and makes a motion as if to stand up, thinks better of it, and continues his melancholy combing.

'What is Life, Uncle Vidna?'

The old man, about to throw a bomb through the window, turns around. 'A searching for something we know we shall not find.'

'Why shall we not find it, Uncle Vidna?' Ivanov's voice is wild in its interrogation.

'We do not know'; and with set face, Uncle Vidna strikes him wearily against the wall time after time.

Or, if you will, turn to poetry. A type much in demand to-day is the satirical free verse made famous by Mr. Osbert Sitwell:

Mrs. Wigmore, known to Chelsea
For the frequency of her Artistic parties
And the undeniable skill which she shows
In making herself as plain as possible
(Beauty, at least in the best circles,
Is quite out of date),
Once gave a Dinner,
Though she called it nothing so suburban,
To Hugo de Hugo
The well-known artist
Who has given up the use of paint entirely
And relies upon sardine-oil and boot-blacking,
Which is so much more natural.
The Dinner was, as Dinners always are,
A perfect success.
Mrs. Wigmore, in her new creation
Of scarlet corduroy,
Made the opening speech,
In which she said,
Her man's voice more intelligible than usual,
That Art, and Life for that matter,
Depended upon the individual's power
To make two and two make five.
This was greeted in the conventional Chelsea manner,
Which consists of taking your neighbour,
By the hair, hand or foot,
Shaking it very hard,
And confessing to an overwhelming admiration
For such an utterly ga-ga remark.
Then the guest of the evening,
Hugo de Hugo,
Born in Kansas City,
Of a Polish mother
And an Australasian engineer,
A small man
With dyed hair and a Palladium accent,
Spoke.

'I am,' he said, 'pleased to be here;
If I were not here
I should be somewhere else, however;
C'est la vie, as Proust says.
I like Mrs. Wigmore,
But I do not think she knows everything about Art.
Art, and Life for that matter,
Is the compression of the Cosmos within the Ego;
Hic ego.'
And sat down.
After that they all drank a toast to Mrs. Wigmore
In methylated spirits.

The patriotic poem is still as popular as ever:

A Flag! ah yes, a flag,
Perchance a faded rag upon a stick;
Yet what tumultuous mem'ries gather thick
And at the heart-strings drag
At view of it! How Fame
At its unfurling grasps her trump and shakes
The drowsy soul to life, and makes
A wonder of a name!
How Duty at the sight
Transforms the city wastrels, country clods,
To eager heroes, rivals of the gods,
And bids them fight the fight.

And, again, the war-poem as Mr. Siegfried Sassoon writes it:

TO THE PROFITEERS

They gave their noble lives for you, my friends,
    Went to their death to save your skin;
You shall repent when this world ends;
    The Lord is down on your type of sin.

And all the men who fought out there and fell,
    Shall sit with maimed and blinded faces near
A hole in Heaven looking down on Hell
    Burning around the Profiteer.

Many of the most successful plays of today have been written around famous people, such as Abraham Lincoln, Charles and Mary, the Barretts of Wimpole Street, etc. This is how it is done:

LUNCH at MUSSOLINI'S

Characters:

    Mussolini.
    His Wife.
    His Son.
    His Daughter.
    His Secretary.

(The breakfast-room of Mussolini's house in Rome. Enter Mussolini. He is wearing his most picturesque uniform and best inscrutable expression. The family springs to attention. He sits. They sit.)

Mussolini (pouring out his coffee): Really, this is too much. My shaving water was cold again. The geyser won't work, and the bathroom's in a perfectly filthy condition.

Wife: Well, what do you expect, dear? If you will keep a machine gun in there?

Mussolini: I have to protect myself, don't I?

Wife: But not in the bathroom, dear.

Mussolini: Bah! (Peels a banana.) Now this banana's bad. Is nothing in this place ever right?

Wife (complacently): No, dear. I hope you remembered to change your underclothing.

Mussolini: I did. And to air my shirt. And do my teeth. And wash behind my ears.

Son: What's father wearing his uniform for today? Is he going to lay a foundation stone or open a public library?

Wife: Hush, dear. He's going to be photographed.

Mussolini (suddenly): Be silent, sir.

(The boy starts to snivel. The women look at one another.)

Wife: Benito!

(No reply.)

Wife: Benito!

Mussolini: Well, what is it? Hasn't that boy got a handkerchief?

Wife: Yes, dear.

Mussolini: Then why doesn't he use it?

(The boy starts snivelling again.)

Mussolini: Can't you see I'm busy? I've an important speech this afternoon.

Wife: Then don't forget your umbrella, dear. It looks like rain.

Mussolini: Bah!

Wife: It's about Edda's new dress.

Mussolini: And do you expect me to discuss such a thing?

Edda: Well, I've got to have one, haven't I?

Mussolini: Don't be impertinent.

Wife: The child's quite right. If we don't hurry we'll be late for the sales.

Mussolini: What's the good of trying to be a dictator when you've got a family?

Wife: I do wish you wouldn't be so violent dear. You almost broke a saucer.

Mussolini: How dare he? How dare he? I'll have him shot. I'll have him torn limb from limb. I'll . . .

Wife: Has someone disagreed with you, dear?

Mussolini: Disagreed! The infernal editor of this rag's had the temerity to criticize me. (Reaches for the bell.)

Wife: Not for a minute, dear. We haven't decided about lunch yet.

Mussolini: Lunch! When the fate of the Empire's trembling in the balance?

Wife: Yes, dear. You won't be late again today, will you?

Mussolini: I don't know. I can't say. Why?

Wife: We shan't be able to keep a maid in the house if you go on being late for meals.

Mussolini: I've never heard of such a thing! You must assert yourself.

Wife: Yes, dear. Perhaps you'd like to begin with the cook?

Mussolini (hurriedly): I . . . eh . . . certainly not. I've enough to do already. (Strikes the bell. Enter Secretary.)

Secretary: Excellency?

Mussolini (pointing at the paper): Have you seen this?

Secretary: Yes, Excellency. The secret police arrested him an hour ago. They want to know what they are to do with him.

Mussolini: Do? We must be lenient. He was an old friend of my father's. Say twenty years imprisonment in a fortress and a fine of three million lire.

Secretary: Very good, Excellency. There's another matter.

Mussolini: Another?

Secretary: Two Germans on the Lido complained about the cooking at their hotel.

Mussolini: Complained about Italian cooking! It's a national insult. Start reprisals with the German Ambassador.

Secretary: Very good, Excellency. (Bows and withdraws.)

Mussolini: That's the way to deal with them. Be firm. Present a bold front. That's where Napoleon . . .

Wife: Yes, dear. But what would you like for lunch?

Mussolini: Lunch! What does it matter? You know I don't care what I eat.

Wife: What about a little vermicelli, then?

Mussolini: Certainly not. We had it on Monday.

Wife: But it's so nourishing; so good for you, dear.

Mussolini: I tell you I won't have vermicelli. We're always having vermicelli.

Wife: Then perhaps you'd think of something for yourself.

Son: Macaroni.

Edda: Shush!

Mussolini: What do you mean, miss? Shush? I suppose I'm allowed to have macaroni if I want to?

Wife: Yes, dear. But remember what happened the last time we had macaroni.

Mussolini: Eh?

Son: Yes, father. You had indigestion and sent the fleet to fight the Greeks.

Mussolini: How dare you? Men have died for saying less than that to me.

Wife: Yes, dear; but what *are* you going to have for lunch?

Mussolini: I tell you I don't mind. Not as long as it's got garlic in it. I've got to make a patriotic speech this afternoon.

Wife: Vermicelli, then?

Mussolini: Bah!

And, lastly, for the sentimental sonnet:

> I shall not come again, nor ever call
>   The swan upon the waveless lake to me,
> To see it sail, with no wing's sound at all,
>   Along the waters of the mimic sea.
>
> I shall not hear the singing birds again;
>   The thrush's voice is, like a sweet ghost, gone
> Out of the warmth into the bitter rain;
>   There are no leaves for me to walk upon.
>
> And I am tired of the too-hot sun
>   Beating upon me till the night brings sleep;
> There is no restfulness, the fierce day done;
>   There is no quiet in the bright-mooned deep.
>
> And by my side I hear the tropic sea
> Lifting its voice like mine, but not to me.

THE POETS OF SWANSEA

This was the over-all title used to describe the first five of the six articles printed continuously here. The sixth (originally titled 'A Modern Poet of Gower') was an additional item; but, since it is very much of the same kind, and deals with another 'local' poet, it is included here with the others. The articles, separated here by Roman numerals, were first published as follows: I—*Herald of Wales*, 9 January 1932, p. 7; II—*ibid.*, 23 January 1932, p. 6; III—*ibid.*, 20 February 1932, p. 4; IV—*ibid.*, 19 March 1932, p. 4; *ibid.*, 23 April 1932, p. 4; VI—*ibid.*, 25 June 1932, p. 8.

I

It is obvious that any survey of Swansea's literary figures and activities within the last hundred years or so cannot be regarded, in any sense, as complete. Many writers are forgotten, sunk out of sight and recognition; many books are lost or difficult to get hold of. What treasures have been thrown into the ash-heap of dead literature it is impossible to imagine, and equally as futile, for criticism is concerned with the living things, however long—and the paradox is justifiable—they may have been dead.

It is necessary to point out the limitations imposed upon these articles, not as a personal apology, but as a general safeguard in case of mis-statement or omission.

The most typical, if not the best, poetry turned out by a Welsh town should be written in Welsh; a local poet should write in the language of his locality. So here again is another limitation, for this survey touches only upon poets who have been born in, or lived in Swansea, and who have written in English. That, of course, rules out many prominent men who have been patriotic enough to use their national tongue.

From Walter Savage Landor, in the early nineteenth century, to Mr. J. C. Woods of today, is a long step, interesting for a number of reasons—historical, poetical and reactionary. The progress of poetry, if progress it can be called, is to be seen spread over a number of years like a literary pageant in miniature, easy to visualise because of its essential narrowness.

Between Landor and Woods stretches a long line of poets. There are Ann Kemble, Joseph Jones, S. P. Chapman, C. D. Morgan, George Thomas Hood, H. A. W. Rott, J. C. Manning, Llewelyn Prichard, James John Evans, E. E., 'Pierre Claire', Zitella Tompkins, Francis Ridley Havergal, 'Liethelba', Glynn Vivian, Gwili, Howard Harris, and many more, who, however minor is their poetry, have definite local and historical appeal.

Swansea's literary associations embrace, too, a number of more or less casual acquaintances—George Borrow, who stayed in the Mackworth Hotel; Edward Thomas, who spent quite considerable periods with the late Mr. John Williams, head-master of Waun Wen School, at Waun Wen; and Thomas Bowdler, the expurgator of Shakespeare, whose last fifteen years were spent in Rhyddings House, afterwards to be made famous by Landor himself.

Borrow's remarks upon Swansea are illuminating, if not complimentary, for in 'Wild Wales' he calls the town a 'large, bustling, dirty, gloomy place', and says of Glandwr, now Landore, that he found himself 'splashed from top to toe there, for the roads were frightfully miry'. He praises the ale, however, and the excellent accommodation afforded him at the Mack-worth Hotel. His was but a passing acquaintanceship with the town, but, even if it left no mark on him, except as he says, on his clothes, his mark will remain upon the town as long as 'Wild Wales' is read and appreciated.

Thomas Bowdler, buried at Oystermouth Cemetery, lived in Rhyddings from 1810 to 1825, the year in which he died, and was appointed, during his last few years, as official inspector of prisons. His chief claim to fame, or notoriety, is his family edition of Shakespeare, the ten volumes of which were com-pleted in Rhyddings House, and published in 1818. The plays, under his merciless editorship, were made fit for nursery and convent, and, to put it in his own words, were purged of those passages considered indelicate or offensive.

It is easy to scoff at Bowdler for pandying to the milk-and-water susceptibilities of the Victorian public; it is easy, too, to call the great amount of work such expurgation entailed, pure humbug. But Swinburne, in his 'Studies in Prose and Poetry', expressed a very sane and balanced attitude when he said of him 'that no man ever did better service to Shakespeare than the man who made it possible to put him into the hands of intelligent and imaginative children'. Personally, I think if Shakespeare is considered too 'strong' for children, they should not read him until they are considered strong enough themselves to withstand him. But there is no doubt Swinburne's attitude, and it is a remarkable one in so explosive and reactionary a writer, is one with which many people agree.

Perhaps Swansea's adoption of Walter Savage Landor as its own poet may be considered impudence in view of the fact that he was born at Warwick, and educated at Ashbourne and Cambridge; lived, for various periods, at Bath, Monmouthshire, and on the continent, and died in Florence. But, the jealous townsman will say, seeing the great figure slip out of his clutch into the welcoming arms of some other town or county, Landor lived in Rhyddings House from 1793 to 1804, meeting Rose Aylmer while he was there, and, on her lending him Clara Reeves's 'Progress of Romance', subsequently publishing his epic poem, 'Gebir', and was influenced by the town and its people more strongly than anyone who is not deeply acquainted with his work could realise.

Rose Aylmer inspired him to write one of the most beautiful and most popular short poems in the language:

> Oh, what avails the sceptered race,
>   Oh, what the form divine!
> What every virtue, every grace!
>   Rose Aylmer, all were thine.
>
> Rose Aylmer, whom these wakeful eyes
>   May weep, but never see,
> A night of memories and sighs
>   I consecrate to thee.

This is great poetry in every sense of the word; not a phrase, not a word, could be altered to its advantage; it is poetry in its strictest, most economical and concentrated form, full of that dignity and chastened splendour Landor instilled into everything he wrote.

His scholarship was as wide as his imagination, and as deep. He had immersed himself in classical literature so much that Mr. Sidney Colvin's definition of him 'as a classic writing in a romantic age' seems almost justified until one realises that this is as much as saying that Landor was born out of his age, a literary freak, a curiosity. If there was one thing he was not, it was a literary phenomenon. He was an exceptionally gifted man, with great classical knowledge and poetical intelligence, who devoted himself to delving into and constructing again some of that classical spirit he found so near and sympathetic to him.

The only argument I have against people who persist in calling him a Swansea poet does not concern itself with a town's natural jealousy and devotion for a great writer, or whether such jealousy is impudence or not. In calling Landor one town's poet, you call him a local poet. Landor is national, international; he should never be localised.

As a contrast, for the name she sometimes wrote under, 'Ann of Swansea', is as fair and just as any she could have adopted, Ann Julia Kemble, sister of Mrs. Sarah Siddons, is the first local writer of anything approaching importance. Not that her contribution towards local literature is valuable; her writings never touched poetry, and just escaped doggerel, but as an historic factor and as a supremely interesting and provocative woman her importance is second to none. She was Swansea's first author, or, at least, the first author recognised by an appreciative public. She was the first writer to link Swansea with the rest of the literary world, and though now she is consigned to shelves and shadows by all her townsfolk, and to many of those she is a name and nothing more, just a name mentioned by some old crank or other grubbing—like a grey mouse in the cellar after books, Ann of Swansea was a very famous woman in her time.

Her first marriage was a tragic failure; it is in some of her poems that the real tragedy can be best appreciated. Sometimes out of the stiff, pretentious artificiality of her verses, beaten out to a metronome in the conventional manner, a phrase, or a line, of real passion and sincerity will burst through like a comet out of the wastes of dull sky. What was suffering in her, broken by companionless marriage, could not be kept under perpetually;

the clichés gave way; the empty words had meaning. But these
bursts were occasional; she managed, on the whole, to keep her
verses on a nice drab level of mediocrity. It would be unnecessary, and rather unkind to quote from her; a quotation would
call for immediate cynicism, deprecatory remarks from our
exalted positions as critics of the twentieth century; and as her
real importance lies in herself and her time and her fame rather
than in her writing, such cynicism is out of place.

Ann Kemble, then Ann Hatton, decided to live in New York,
and stayed there, trying to drown her troubles in the fashionable gaiety and snobbery of the time until she heard of her
husband's death. She came back to Wales and later married
Mr. Curtis, with whom she lived for the rest of her life. She
sometimes wrote under the name of Ann of Kidwelly, but it is as
Ann of Swansea, bound up in her own town, bound up in her
own people, that she will go down into the annals of Swansea
history.

Chronologically, Samuel Palmer Chapman, grandfather of
the present High-street photographer, is not the next poet who
should be considered for his literary and local interest; his book,
'Stolen Minutes with the Muses', was published in 1877,
approximately fifty years after the publication of Bowdler,
Landor, and Ann Kemble. But Chapman's poetical trifles were
written, and it is that with which we are concerned, nearly forty
years before he printed them for private circulation. The
majority of them were composed about 1829, four years after
'Imaginary Conversations' burst upon the intellectual world
with all its strength and splendour, and four years before Ann
dedicated her 'Miscellaneous Poems' to Her Grace the Duchess
of Devonshire.

To talk of Samuel Chapman after a writer of Landor's genius
and a personage of Ann Kemble's fame, may seem too much of
an anti-climax. But I am considering Chapman individually;
I am not linking him with anyone else, but am continuing the
survey of Swansea writers in as chronological and unprejudiced
a manner as possible.

Chapman was born at Waddington in 1809, the fifteenth
child of an even more extensive family, and until he was seven-
teen years of age was unable to read a chapter in the New
Testament—his only reading book—without spelling several

words. He was a bad writer, a worse speller, and was almost oblivious to the mystery of hyphening. It is, therefore, distinctly to his credit that as a young man he wrote as much, and as good, poetry as many young men who have had the advantage of a more rigorous education. 'Before I was 20'—I am allowing him to speak for himself—'my first incentive to write poetry was the all prevailing one of love. Bright little Phoebe! I was over "head and ears", as the saying is, and wanted, of course, to write to her in poetry, but not having read any, the task was above my utmost powers. What was to be done? I had a few coppers in my pocket, and the next time I went to town I would invest them in poetry on love.' The first book he bought was Defoe's satire of the 'True Born Englishman', the second 'The Deserted Village', and the third—each with a space, for financial reasons, between them—was Ovid's 'Art of Love'. These completed his poetical education.

The main impression his verses give are those of a benevolent and lovable personality shining through the worn-out phrases of a worn-out poetry. It is hard to be destructive in one's criticism of such obvious sincerity, such obvious love of youth, 'and all its attendant tears and laughter', its devotion to ideals and causes that, however much they may be out of favour to-day, can never quite be drowned beneath the waves of sophistication and iconoclasm. But it is equally hard to be anything but destructive; it is the man whose sincerity and devotion one cannot help admire, not the poet. Samuel Chapman looked on the world with the eyes of an artist, but his poetical accomplishments were insufficient to portray, with any clarity, what he saw.

II

No one can deny that the most attractive figures in literature are always those around whom a world of lies and legends has been woven, those half mythical artists whose real characters become cloaked for ever under a veil of the bizarrre. They become known not as creatures of flesh and blood, living day by day as prosaically as the rest of us, but as men stepping on clouds, snaring a world of beauty from the trees and sky, half wild, half human.

It is, on the whole, a popular and an entertaining fallacy.

But Llewelyn Prichard was a genuine figure of fancy. The gaunt wide-eyed poet with the wax nose, might have stepped from the pages of a romanticist's diary. His life, strange and disordered, as poet, artist, and strolling player, trembling on the verge of disease, one foot in the grave and the other in the workhouse, needs no glossing over. With Prichard, eccentricity was no pose; it was not bestowed upon him by contemporaries; it was ingrained in the man.

He was born in the parish of Tralling, Breconshire, and, dying in Major Roteley's cottage, Thomas-street, World's end, Swansea, was buried in the Wesleyan Tabernacle, St. John-street. Neither the date of his birth nor his death is certain, and his last days were spent in the utmost degradation and poverty. Little is known of his actual life, and his books are not informative; he seemed to create in his poetry an impersonal attitude, to break down the remorseless introspection that sent his mind fluttering on the edge of insanity. He kept his mind balanced, to a certain degree, by the vast amount of work he turned out, especially between 1820 and 1830, when his output included romances, guides, anthologies, novels, and many books of poems, all, however, conventionally worded, full of an intense energy convention could not kill, and bright with a fire poverty could not diminish in any way. Indeed, as life became harder for him, so did his poems become stronger in resolve, gain in power, and lost much of that imitativeness which, along with verbose sentimentality, were the chief characteristics of early Nineteenth Century verse.

Prichard, under the *nom de théâtre* of Jeffrey Llewelyn, toured the largest towns in West Wales along with a theatrical company, whose repertoire included some of the most melodramatic plays conceivable. He performed at the Brecon Theatre in 1841, and at the Assembly Rooms, Aberystwyth, in the same year. There is a story concerning his stay at Aberystwyth which goes to say that when the company arrived in the town they found they had lost their printing press, and could not print any bills. They had the type properly set and the paper ready, so every time the moistened paper was laid on the inked type, Prichard, the heaviest of the players, had to sit on the paper until the process was finished.

There is no record as to whether Prichard was a good or a

bad actor; he would, at any rate, have been a remarkable figure upon the stage, being over six foot tall and proportionately broad, with thin features and lustrous eyes. He had lost his nose in a duel many years before he took up the stage as a profession, and now, comically sticking from his tragedian's face, was a large, turned-up wax nose. 'Would to God', he once said, pointing at his nose, 'the second artist had been as clever as the first,' but though he often ridiculed his own deformity, it was a source of painful and terrible self-consciousness to him. When, in later years, he lived like a hermit in the ruins of the Gate House, once in Wassail-square, near St. Mary's Church, the taunts of the children who would not leave him alone, but ran after him jeering and shrieking at his heels, drove him near to madness. It was because of the children that he moved from the ruined house to Thomas-street: men he was not afraid of; he was indifferent to their cruelty, but the sharp cries of the children, and the spite and vehemence with which they clung to him, was more than he could bear. More, too, than he could understand, for even in his drunkenest moods, and he drank, as he did everything else, fiercely and intemperately, no thought of cruelty would come into his head.

'Twm Shon Catti' should be more widely known outside Wales than it is, for Prichard has created in his hero an adventurer as boisterous as Gargantua and as spirited as Robin Hood. Indeed, an edition published in England called him 'the Welsh Robin Hood', but Twm Shon Catti, even while the comparison is fair, needs no comparative value thrown upon his own escapades. He is a figure of the imagination, wildly improbable and highly delightful, one of the few characters in Welsh literature that deserves to take its place among the immortals.

The original of Prichard's portrait of this unorthodox and lawless gentleman is said to be Thomas Jones, poet and genealogist, who was born about 1530, a son, not of Sir John Wynn of Gwyder, as is commonly supposed, but of John, son of David ap Madog ap Howel Maethen, and Catherine, daughter of Meredydd ap Ieuan. Thomas Jones, like his fictitious descendant, placed no value upon the rules and regulations of the land, and led the life of an outlaw for many years. Later he was pardoned, however, and his last days were devoted to the study of Welsh history and literature. Whether

he is the original of Twm Shon Catti or not is of little importance; whether Prichard's character was founded on truth or
not, does not detract from the energy and vigour of the story;
it is a little point, however interesting it may be, to dig into
history with one's little shovel and bring to light the most
curious and the most futile facts.

'The Heroines of Welsh History, comprising memoirs and
biographical notices of the celebrated women of talent, the
exemplary of conduct, the eccentric in character, and the
curious by position, or otherwise,' was never all published.
Prichard wrote both volumes in World End Cottage, and
persuaded William Morris, of the Stamp Office, High-street, to
publish it. The first volume met with little success, and the
second volume, which Prichard left with his friend, the inn-
keeper at the Red Cow, High-street, has never come to light.
The first volume was dedicated, quaintly enough, to 'Virtuous
Votaries of True Womanhood, in all its Graces, Purity and
Excellence, as contra-distinguished from the Fantastic Fooleries
and Artificial Characteristics of Fine Ladyism in the Middle
Walks of Life'. It is a huge work, written perhaps in too
pompous and stilted a style, but nevertheless, full of interest to
the antiquarian and the lover of literature.

His books of poetry—and much of it is—include 'Mariette
Mouline, or the Death of Glyndower', printed in 1823, by W.
Hersee, White Lion Court, Cornhill, and 'Welsh Minstrelsey,
containing the Land Beneath the Sea, or Cartref y Gwaelod',
published by John and Hunt, Covent Garden, 1824. He edited
also 'A Selection of English Poems on Welsh Subjects, Original
and Translated from the Cambro British', called 'The Cambrian Wreath, by various editors of celebrity, living and
departed'. This was printed by John Cox at Aberystwyth, in
1828, the same year as 'Twm Shon Catti' appeared. This is an
exceptionally rare volume, containing as it does some curious
drawings by Prichard himself.

His 'Guide to Aberystwyth', which was printed at Aberystwyth in 1824, and sold also in London, Bath, Cheltenham,
Shrewsbury, Birmingham, Worcester, Hereford, Bala and
Carmarthen, is the most exhaustive ever published, and still
allows Prichard room for many of his philosophic, and more
often than not, sententious generalisations.

Towards the end of his life Prichard's poverty became so
great, and his physical reserves so low, that Samuel Chapman,
his loyalest friend and greatest admirer, made a collection
around the town to keep him from the Union Workhouse.
Chapman's efforts succeeded; but, like many such actions,
were soon to seem futile. Prichard, coming home late one night
to the cottage in Thomas-street, attempted to write in his own
room. But he soon fell asleep. The candle fell on to the papers
surrounding him. His clothes caught fire. He was too drunk to
know what to do, and died as strangely and as tragically as he
had lived, 'caught in a chaos of unrestrained words and
passions, caught by the fire and the flames'.

> Will not our sons—in indignation bold—
> Scorn us, as we our guilty sires of old;
> In these brief words our sad neglect deride:
> He starved in Swansea, and in Swansea died.

These are the words of Samuel Chapman; and these the words
of Llewelyn Prichard himself, on the verge of lunacy, fighting
with all his weakened strength to remain outside the workhouse:

> In scorn and hunger I would rather die
> Than in the Union close each failing eye;
> Let me have liberty, or nothing give,
> For losing that, at once I cease to live.
> Though hunger urges, all I ask and crave
> Is, not to fill a wretched pauper's grave.

The pity of it is that he did.

Out of all the spinsters and thin-lipped amateurs spinning
their little webs of sound, the versifiers, linking cliché to cliché
with metrical perfection, the bards and the old gentlemen; out
of all the poetical products of a small town, Prichard stands out
flaming and aloof against the horizon. He failed to be great, but
he failed with genius.

III

Up to this, the third article in a survey of all those who have
contributed, in one way or another, to the literary history of

Swansea, I have dealt at some length with five writers, Bowdler, Landor, Ann of Swansea, Chapman, Prichard. With the exception of Chapman, these are all important figures: Bowdler, a man of fame; Landor, a man of genius; Anne Kemble, the first Swansea poetess to achieve anything outside parochial renown; and Prichard, a tragic failure, whose life and work it is hard not to romanticise. But with the poets of the middle-Victorian period, all the values I have tried to impose upon the previous essays must go by the board. With J. C. Manning, C. D. Morgan, John Evans, H. A. W. Rott, E. E., and the rest of their contemporaries, it is obviously necessary to change perspective.

I have tried to treat Landor and Prichard as poets and not as celebrities; I have tried to treat them intelligently, not lowering the standard of criticism because the circle of writers before me is so essentially narrow. It would be an insult to Landor, Prichard and Mr. Chapman Woods—to mention only three whose work was written seriously and should be taken seriously —if I treated James John Evans, the blind boy of Mumbles, in the same spirit as I do them. I am up against sentiment. Who is hard-hearted enough to dismiss the sick-bed verses of a diseased child with a phrase, or a disparaging comment on the relationship between chopped prose and carven poetry, between inanity and originality, between the brain that amuses itself with words, and the brain that has to express itself in them? So, although both John Evans and Savage Landor are included in this survey, admirers of the poet, and friends of the blind boy, will have no cause for complaint. I make no association between Landor and Evans, for there is absolutely none.

James John Evans lived at Mumbles. His only book was published in 1884 by Parry, at 52, Oxford-street. Its introduction, written by Mr. Samuel, of Newton, acquaints us with some of the facts concerning the boy—that he was the youngest son of John Evans, tailor and draper, of the Mumbles; that he was blind from birth, and suffered rheumatic pains in hands and body; that he was sent to London to learn basket-making; but that his bodily afflictions made any manual work at all impossible; and that he returned to his home, even more hopeless, more chastened, and perhaps more ready to die.

From then on he led the life of an invalid, whiling away those agonising hours of pain and darkness by writing verses, simple, domestic, devotional, in a copy-book. He had no intention of publishing them, and it may have been, regarded in a later light, cruel for his friends to expose those immature gropings after ideas, those hymn-book phrases, and that utter sterility of intellect the little rhymes showed.

What can one say on reading in one poem?—

> 'Tis eighteen years now
> Since father has been dead;
> A long, long toil of widowhood
> Mother's had for our daily bread.

So crudely expressed, so useless. And yet again, taken literally, too pitiful to decry. Why, then, is it printed for the historian to see, to pull to shreds, to uncover its last decent garment and leave bare for the merciless eyes of the world?

The verses of C. D. Morgan owe a lot less to the hymn-book, and a good deal more to the stereotype work of his contemporaries. They are, of course, entirely lacking in merit, and to anyone but the chronicler of persons and events, worth nothing at all. But he had obviously read some poetry, and in some stanzas of his own catches quite successfully a faint echo of William Wordsworth and Mrs. Hemans.

Morgan was a Gower postman, who wrote an entertaining series of scenes and anecdotes of the countryside called 'Wanderings in Gower', which showed him as a kind, old gossip-monger, with the journalist's eyes for the quaint and curious in rural life. But in his perambulations with Erato he shows himself to be less happy.

> Her eyes are weary with weeping now,
> There's a clammy hand on her snowy brow,
> And back to her bleeding, bursting soul
> The burning waters of agony roll

cannot be excused even though his prefatory remarks make it clear that the poems 'are the strugglings of an infant muse, and are laid most humbly before the reader.' 'The author is aware,' he goes on to say, 'of his temerity in attempting to climb the heights of Parnassus, but he trusts he will be spared the critics' censure when the unpretending nature of the little volume is considered.'

The verses are not unpretending. They try to persuade the reader he is reading into passion, while all the time he is reading into nothing.

> Language fails me, when I come to
> breathe my fervent love to thee,
> And, like an infant, weak I feel now
> can this, can this be?
> Each pulse thrills, quivers, trembles,
> when thy lovely face is nigh,
> O for one sweet smile, my dearest,
> one glance from thy bright eye.

Language indeed fails him.

H. A. W. Rott, the father of the present engraver in Orange-street, and who was himself one of the first men in the litho-graphic trade, came to Swansea in 1862. He had been brought up by his cousin, the Bishop Woodford, which, according to his sons, accounts for the poetical temptations he alone, of all the family, succumbed to. He published his only book of verse, 'Fugitive Pieces', at his shop at Lower Oxford-street, in 1883. He was the real small-town versifier, turning out rhymes on important urban occasions with great complacency and dis-regard for metre. But he was a cheerful optimist, and after the glut of Victorian melancholia, it is pleasant to read his bright unprepossessing lines:

> The Summer comes,
> With days so warm and bright,
> When the bee hums,
> And the hawthorn blossoms
> And the butterfly roams,
> And new mown hay the air around perfumes;
> The rose blossoms,
> And all is gay, and there is scarcely night.

It is good, too, to hear one voice greeting the New Year like this:

> Hail, New Year! I greet thee hopefully,
> Trust thou hast blessing in store for me,
> Blessing for all, the small and the great.
> Blessing for England, her people and state,
> Blessing for every nation on earth,
> Blessing from God who doth give blessing birth.

His official verses are almost invariably adulatory, as when he writes on the Royal visit to Swansea, October 18, 1887:

> Swansea, be joyous, make fit preparation,
> Welcome with honour the Prince of the Nation;
> He comes here on purpose to open our Dock!
> Be ready to meet him! Of cheers have a stock.

It is obvious here, at least, that the urgency of the rhyme dictated whatever sense there is. It would be easy to demolish his verses with an epithet. But he is so optimistic, so ingenuous.

'The Death of Saul', Carl Morgannwg's poem, won the first prize at the Wrexham National Eisteddfod in 1876, and was published, along with some shorter poems, by the author himself at Castle-street in 1878. J. C. Manning, to use Morgannwg's real name, was a man deeply versed in the Miltonic tradition. His 'Death of Saul' was, as the Vicar of Wrexham said in his adjudicatory remarks, 'written in a style well adapted to the subject, in language dignified and sonorous, with spacious images and phrases, real poetry, suggestive and deeply impressive—the poetry of thought and culture rather than of mere figure and fancy.'

After such a grand eulogy it is with timidity I confess that for me, at any rate, much of the poem is dull and dry. But not all. The end is quite beautiful, when:

> The soul of Saul went drifting through the dark
> Like some fair ship with sails and cordage rent;
> And then the cry of lamentation rose
> In Israel, and the Hebrew maidens hung
> Their speechless harps upon the willow branch,
> And mourned the loved and lost unceasingly.

In another short poem, too, he shows himself quite capable of putting by the organ for the flute:

> She came in beauty like the sun,
> And flushed with hope each heart and eye,
> As roses redden into life
> When Summer passes by.

Manning is a satisfactory poet, a man of discernment and learning, who knew his Byron as well as his Milton.

I am left with 'E. E.' and George Thomas Hood. 'E. E.' was an invalid lady who spent much of her time in Caswell. She published her two books of verse anonymously between 1850 and 1860. They are jingles, pure and simple. Some make sense. Some don't. George Thomas Hood was another invalid, who died from consumption in 1872. He was then aged 23. If he had lived longer he might have written something really worth while. The roots were there, but the tree had not time to grow.

IV

The 19th century closes. Browning, for the last time, drops his theorbo and Tennyson's brook has stopped running. Swinburne, Rossetti, and, across the water, Rimbaud and Verlaine are dead. The Yellow Poets, complete with black hat and absinthe, are sedulously pruning what Baudelaire has left of Les Fleurs du Mal. Arnold, dignified old academician, has sunk into posterity. The great ones are gone, out of one unreal world into another, the great ones are dead.

But here, rising from this respectable town, is the voice of Pierre Claire, Mr. S. C. Camwell, editor of a most respectable paper. The vulgarity, the voluptuousness of the Naughty Nineties leaves no mark upon him, serenely and chastely he turns out his verses, and lays them at the feet of the Local Muse. Camwell was, first and last, a journalist, not of the old school, but of the new school. His poetry was Victorian in the least complimentary sense of the word; his philosophy is based upon theological commonplaces. But—and this is what made his writing popular, this is where his literary interest lies—nearly every verse he wrote was a news paragraph. He fell into writing as another man falls into picking pockets, easily and inevitably. The little things which caught his attention, the gossip, the odd irrelevancies, local ceremonies, public occasions, pleas and protests on behalf of local concerns, all these he put into metre, marking the parish-pump with the hands of the true journalist.

A young seaman, nephew of the Mayor of Swansea, is accidentally drowned while sculling a boat in the waters of the East Dock. For an ordinary newspaper man this is a paragraph; and, possibly, a remark upon the young man's great charm of personality, or prowess at football, or whatever qualification the dead man has to proffer at the gates of Heaven. But Camwell was no ordinary reporter, and, later, no ordinary editor. The tragedy gives him an opportunity to write:

> The drowned seaman sleeps imperially
> In ocean's tranquil depths, where tempest's roar
> Wakes him to doubt or danger never more!
> Less happy, for less happy fate hath he
> Who, in the shelter of his destined port,
> Young, strong and willing-hearted, proud to be
> A merchant mariner, both life cut short—
> Drowned within reach of help, most piteously.

It is no mean gift being able to turn a piece of news into a nice, platitudinary set of verses, made to please relatives and poet-tasters alike.

Ellen Sweeney, who was, at one time, Queen of Swansea night-life, celebrates her two hundred and twenty fifth conviction for drunkenness. The same night Camwell prints an imaginary conversation with her, in which she says:

> Convicted Sir? I've been convicted
> Two hundred and twenty-five times.
> Lord love you, you need not shrink from me—
> It wasn't for very dark crimes.
> I never did nothing to no one
> To hurt 'em. Some high people wink
> At sins in themselves just as dreadful;
> My fault is a drop too much drink.

He goes on to turn public sympathy in her favour, lends her a
certain dramatic fatalism the old woman was never sober
enough to know she possessed. She says, in an almost indecent
orgy of self-pity:

> Look here, Sir, it don't stand to reason,
> Now do it? I'm nobody's wife,
> Nor am I the mother of children,
> And most of my natural life
> I've spent in her Majesty's prison.
> God bless her! God save the good Queen!
> They say she's a kind sort of woman;
> But a rag and a blackguard I've been.

She goes on to say, in the hoarse voice adoped by drawing-
room elocutionists:

> 'Tis true. 'Tis as true as the scripture.
> Yes; I have been always a fool.
> I'm a nuisance, I know, and a gaol-bird,
> But I wasn't a dunce when at school.
> There's some who, today, are respected.
> And hold up their heads in the town,
> And live in fine houses, that need not
> On poor Ellen Sweeney look down.

There is a sinister threat in those last four lines that possibly
brought a blush of shame to more than one of what she would
call 'the fine ladies' of Swansea.

Neither of the quotations is a good example of what Camwell
could write when he broke the limitations of locality, and
attempted to embrace the outer and inner world of humanity,
but they show him as a superb journalist. He could turn the
tide of public opinion with a few verses, better than a
rhetorician. He could, with a piece of doggerel, influence,
create, destroy, deride, what he wished. Sanely, and with
abundant humour and common-sense, he could sway the
public sentiments any way he wanted, fan their indignation,
voice their triumphs, allay their fears. He made his poems—
and 'The Cambrian',—a mirror of what the public thought,
and, more important still, a mirror of what they looked like.

He wrote with common sense, while his poetic brothers, the Swinburnes, and the Dowsons of the period, were content to write with genius. Oddly enough, he became strange as he became older, his great gift of commonsense eventually deserting him, and leaving him at the end subject to long fits of depression. It was an unfitting end to such a sensible life. He should have died, haloed in respectability, waiting with ordinary fear, for death to come. Instead of that the last days of his life were filled with terror. Like George the First, he cried out 'Why did you not tell me death was terrible? Why did you not tell me?'

V

Poetry has been called an attitude towards life, a definition that has a certain amount of truth in it, and yet will not bear anything more than the most casual scrutiny, for while the poetry of a Rossetti was the outcome of one dark mood, and all his creations, in words or paint, part of one narrow introspective attitude, there is, as certainly as Rossetti, the poet who critically destroys what he sees in life, the poet who rhymes what he visualises; none of these, and there are a thousand different species of the literary animal, regards poetry as an attitude.

James Chapman Woods can be placed in a rarer and more distinguished category; his poetry is, like Arnold's, a criticism of life; he looks at life with an intellectual eye, looks at it from many angles, turns his head away, contemplates, then, with a fine chastity of phrase, and an almost classical lucidity of speech, sums life up. This ability to criticise in verse is a definite poetical accomplishment. But poetry needs more than that. A poet needs more than a merely analytical brain; he is not a lawyer; he is a creator and must contribute to life as well as dissect it.

Mr. Woods has much to offer beside his critical, or, if you will, his surgical skill; he has a vocabulary steeped in classical tradition, and an ear for the secret magic of words. He is a scholar, which accounts for much; he is an accomplished metrician. But these are not the things that will take him to heaven; skill and learning will not link him hand in hand with Shelley, Blake and Keats, stepping shadowy from dark to light; rather will they leave him in the dark, tied back to back with

Matthew Arnold, and the dark figures of the early twentieth century poets.

The editor of the 'East Anglian Anthology', to which Mr. Woods contributed a number of poems, says: 'The poems of Mr. James Chapman Woods are remarkable for their nice balance of feeling and intellect. They are essentially the work of a scholar. They are the expression, not of what is tumultuous, fervid, ecstatic, or transcendental, but of quiet thought and deep feeling.' Although more like an obituary notice than a passage of criticism, that does help to show Mr. Woods writes good poetry.

It is that balance of feeling and intellect that prevents Mr. Woods from getting away from his perpetual atmosphere of self-conscious serenity. His verse is too balanced, and is conscious of its balance all the time; what is lacking is the warmth of personality, the strange individual glow which lights up everything beautiful enough to be remembered.

His first book of poems, 'A Child of the People', published by Kegan Paul in 1879, is, quite naturally, a volume of imitations. Most first volumes are, but Mr. Woods's unlike some, never sank into parody, and had, on occasions, an originality of diction which proved too much for a contemporary critic, who, declining to go far in their depths, described the poems as very good, but melancholy, disregarding the fact that to condemn a poet on the grounds of melancholia is as futile as condemning a comedian for being comic.

The octet in the last sonnet of 'A Child of the People' is worth reading aloud in order to appreciate the interwoven music of the words:

> I, singer, ere I grow unmusical,
> Sing now the last lay I have heart to sing.
> Glad of my life of love time that was Spring.
> Of labour that is summer tide and fall;
> Nor much a dread of death, earned rest of all,
> Save of the death of no remembering;
> I crown my cairn, each stone a song, and bring
> All of my life I love for burial.

There is a promise of genius about those lines which was never realised, for the poems, gaining in intellect, lost in heart. Those lines, too, are original in the sense that they owe little to any poet except, perhaps, Gerard Manley Hopkins, the Catholic priest.

There are, in these early poems, wedged between lines that any contemporary could have written, phrases and lines of a remarkable verbal beauty. Mr. Woods has always kept an eye on Arnold's dictum concerning the necessity for having some great traditional phrases as touchstones when writing original poetry. So when he writes: 'When Love the lily-handed fought with death', it does not mar the beauty of the line to know that lily-handed was one of Robert Greene's concoctions, or that Sacheverell Sitwell has made the phrase, many years later than Mr. Woods, even more beautiful as 'the lily-wristed morn'. When he says: 'This year I have not heard the cuckoo call', in the opening of a sonnet, a hundred similarly wistful lines come to the memory.

He had, and has, all the poets at his fingertips, and need only move his hand for the beautiful words and the beautiful lines to come to him, can summon at will the great phrases of the world, has, leaning over his shoulder, a number of famous ghosts, who talk to him and, very kindly, advise him. He can ride, even with these ghosts of his:

> We rode to Camelot, I and he
> It was the time of Spring turned lover.
> A wind, caught in the greenery,
> Shredded with glancing shafts the cover.

With such literary company, Mr. Woods can never be alone.

In this first volume he was creative on a basis of tradition. He had his models, but was not content to copy them. They were there to remind him where tradition began, and the genuine beauty of some of these early poems gives promise of a poetical future that would, in time, drop all traditional fetters and find freedom, and a personal originality fit to compare with any of the late 19th century. But 'The Youth of Arcady', published in 1912, marked the end of his creative activities. That book of poems was the final splutter of his romanticism.

His last book, 'A Pageant of Poets', shows him in all his

mature logic and scholarship; it shows the critical mind at its
best, but it is not what a reader of 'A Child of the People'
would expect. 'A Pageant of Poets' is Mr. Woods's most
accomplished volume; his style is more careful and more
ornate than that of any living writer, and his thoughts are the
thoughts of an old man, deep, unruffled, unprejudiced, but
suspicious of the changing 'whirligig of taste', leisurely but still
concentrated.

He has immersed his personality into the personalities of his
masters so completely that he will never regain it. He is, now,
a mirror of what the traditional masters of poetry have and
would have written. He talks of Landor, and says:

> The art of Life, the life of Art, he scanned
> And moulded as the pattern to his hand.
> The life of Athens in its golden age,
> Of Tuscan gardens under rambling bines,
> Repeopled with Boccaccio's Florentines,
> Of Arden before Shakespeare stormed the stage.

Of Keats he writes:

> Still thy receding voice the nightingale,
> Deep in the brooding thicket's shadowy nest,
> Remembers in each midnight of its June;
> When Art revives the harmonies
> Of Attic life and grace on plinth and frieze,
> Thine are the unaging lips that flute the tune.

One could go indefinitely through these delightful eulogies, and
find, in every one, Mr. Woods's essential sanity, the way he can
get at the heart of a poet in so few lines.

It is his professional life that has altered the trend of his own
poetry from a dark and passionate beauty, caught sometimes in
'A Child of the People', and more often in the following
sonnets, to such a judicial complacence, when his masters fit so
fairly and evenly into the water-tight compartments he has
fashioned for them; when Walter Scott is

> Supremest bearer of his country's name,
> Rekindling the deserted border-land.

When Shelley is 'truant from the ranks of light'; Browning, 'Poet of the towering intellect, lord of the analytics of the mind'; Elizabeth Barrett, 'A weakling woman with a seraph's face, and tone and pity in her tender eyes'; Arnold, 'Clear voice of melancholy doubt'; and Swinburne, but this time clumsily called, 'Captain of rhythm and sound'.

There they are, labelled and unmistakable. The whole pageant is literally a procession of great, or, allowing for personal prejudices, famous figures gilded for the public eye, made glorious with the colours of poetical language dipped in the honey of a thousand years. There they pass, Landor, Southey, Coleridge, Wordsworth, Scott, Byron, Shelley, Keats, the Brownings, Tennyson, Arnold, Rossetti, William Morris, Swinburne, and that dignified old commentator James Chapman Woods. That is, surely, a fit destiny for him to be linked, though he has no call to greatness, along with the great, a man who has appreciated, valued, and mirrored what the undying poets have said.

VI

It is curious that the wonders of Celtic mythology, and the inexplicable fascination that Welsh legends are bound to exercise upon whoever takes enough trouble to become acquainted with them, have not influenced the Anglo-Welsh poets more considerably.

W. H. Davies, the most gifted Welsh poet writing in English today, could, if he had chosen, have made something very great out of the legends of his own country. He could have recreated the fantastic world of the Mabinogion, surrounded the folk lore with his own fancies, and made his poetry a stepping place for the poor children of darkness to reach a saner world where the cancer of our warped generation is no more than a pleasant itch. But he preferred to follow in the direct line of the hedgerow poets, leaning over some country stile with placid expression, thinking of nothing more edifying than the brevity of life, the green of the grass, and the inanity of personal expression.

Howard Harris, born at Swansea, educated at Dynevor Place, and the Belfast and Aberystwyth Universities, is a small poet with a large ambition. His romantic verses are not particularly distinguished, but they contribute more to the revival of Welsh poetry than any writings I know. They recall much of its most charming folk lore, and show signs of a cultured mind trying to recapture a little, at least, of the Welsh magic now dead as King Arthur. Mr. Harris, taking upon himself the burden that W. H. Davies neglected or refused, is faced with the terrible apathy of the Welsh public. I do not say 'reading' public, because generalisations are apt to lose much of their point if they are applied to a section of the community almost too small to be noticed. Mr. Harris is giving the benefit of a sensitive and trained mind, and the fruits of a number of years' extensive study, towards the culture of Wales.

He is the first poet of Gower. He has shown that the romantic mind is never at a loss to find romance. If the real world cannot give it to him then the world of princesses and giants can. He does not need to find refuge in exotics (although I believe he is interested in them). He has enough imagination to transform the smoking stacks of Landore, as he writes in one of his latest poems, into the 'domes and minarets of Ispahan'. He has enough courage to think his own country beautiful, and not to wish his summers spent in Deauville or the Levant, like the many artistic ostriches who hide their heads in the sand so that they may forget their own countries, and eventually find they have formed a national community of exiles.

But perhaps Mr. Harris states Mr. Harris's literary importance better than I can. 'Until the spirit of a people overflows its own boundaries it can only have a parochial influence,' he writes, 'and until it finally finds its way into the broad current of world culture it but resembles that stream in an area of inland drainage which is lost in the sands instead of the sea.' That is his justification for Anglo-Welsh poetry, it is also his justification for himself. He attempts to kindle 'the race-consciousness of the Welshmen who speak no Welsh, and extend the Celtic message to the widespread English-speaking peoples'. It is a splendid ambition. But—to use the same figure—the Welsh people are content rather to paddle in the stagnant ponds of their own ignorance than swim in Mr. Harris's national sea.

Taken as an artist and not as an internationalist, Mr. Harris can be called a romantic who has found the ideal themes for romance. Artistically, he has done them credit, but not justice. Only a great writer can give this absurd country, full of green fields and chimney stacks, beauty and disease, the loveliness of the villages and the smoke-ridden horror of the towns, its full value and recognition. Gower, his special literary property, calls for the hand of a Corot, and the mind of a Keats. Mr. Harris can give it learning. He can give it the weight of tradition, and the reactions of a sensitive mind. But that is all. His chief fault is his overwhelming love for clichés. He feels a new sensation, thinks of a new beauty, stretches out his hands for notes to express it—and finds a common chord. That is continually happening in his verses. He starts well, gains in intensity, and falls in a single phrase, to the murkiest depths of bathos.

Now he is original, romantic, writing in the grand manner about the questing of Kilwch:

> Who is this youth that pricks forth on a steed
> All dappled grey, firm-limbed, four winters old,
> With golden bridle and fair shell-formed hoofs
> Whose are the hands that hold the silver spears,
> Wounding the wind and causing blood to flow
> As falls the dewdrop from the grass of June?
> Whose hounds are these, white-breasted and keen-eyed,
> With collars of the ruby red and warm,
> Like two sea swallows sporting by his side?

And later, in the same poem, we learn, ''Tis that hot lover Kilwch', a fact indisputable but so absurdly expressed that that which goes before and after that line loses much of its beauty. Constantly such lines as

> Whiter than the curled sea-foam was
> the maiden's heaving bosom,

and

> Keep from the roads of Gower
> If you would Gower see;
> The secret of its power,
> Its true felecitee,

are cropping up with supreme self-confidence, as if the author really thought they could mean anything at all. Mr. Harris has immersed himself too much in other people's poetry, a common failing among scholars, and subsequently has great difficulty in expressing his thoughts in any but other people's words.

But that is the end of adverse criticism. Taking it into consideration, and neglecting to read some of the colloquial verses which he should never have written, there is much that is delightful to look for in his four volumes—'An Exile's Lute' (1919), 'The Harp of Hiraeth' (1922), 'Songs in Shot Silk' (1924), and 'Singing Seas' (1926). He has, among other things, a command of metre and form that many better poets would be proud to possess, a varied vocabulary, and a vein of genuine fancy that gives radiance to the most common flower. Like every writer in the world, he must be read to be appreciated— a statement not even the most controversial enemy of mine could deny. The frills and vapours of literary criticism, while they satisfy the critic and often delude the public, should not be taken too seriously. Critics must live, and many a literary person would murder his mother for an epigram.

Mr. Harris is a schoolmaster. Therefore poetry is merely his hobby. He may have taken to literature as another man takes to fretwork. I do not think that for a moment. But it may be so. It does not, however, mar the fact that he should start taking his poetry more seriously than he does, and begin to forget much of his international theorising. His last book is immeasurably better than his first, and there is every reason to think his next will be better again, which means he is a progressive poet.

Mr. Harris, as a man of intellect, should realise that his way does not lie along the 'open road' upon which Mr. Davies, Mr. Masefield, and, occasionally, Mr. Gerald Gould, lavish such loving care. Mr. Harris is not a song writer. He is not a realist, despite his comparatively successful 'Cross Keys' poem. He is, first and last, a craftsman whose inspiration springs from the myths and legends of his own country, and it is as an anti- quarian and a romanticist that he should develop. But he must take care and time, weeding the hackneyed phrases from his verse, and concentrating upon it neither as a pastime nor a study, but as a work of art. Let him do these things sincerely, and he may eventually find himself the most prominent figure among the Anglo-Welsh writers of today.

GENIUS AND MADNESS AKIN IN WORLD OF ART

From *South Wales Evening Post*, 7 January 1933, p. 7.

The borderline of insanity is more difficult to trace than the majority of people, comparatively safe within the barriers of their own common-sensibility, can realise. And it is even more difficult to differentiate, with any sureness, between insanity and eccentricity.

Someone has said that the thinkers of the world are those whom the rest of mankind call mad, and G. K. Chesterton, a paragon of good sense, firmly believes that a person can get a better view of things when standing on his head than in any other position. That may be. But no one can deny that among the most inspired people of the world there have been enough 'kinks' to satisfy the most disgruntled of modern psychologists.

William Blake, a great poet and artist, was in the habit of sitting, entirely without clothes, in the back of his garden, undismayed by the horror of his neighbours. Swinburne, around whom a great number of legends has grown, continually executed barbaric dances in front of his mirror, snorting and prancing around the room for hours, and was most indignant when anyone interrupted him.

There are thousands of similar examples of eccentricity among men who, in their own spheres of creation or analysis, have shown an amazing sanity and breadth of vision. Oscar Wilde, another almost legendary figure, dressed for long periods in Restoration costume, with high frilled collars and lace breeches. It was among the sights of London to see him walking, thus garbed, through Piccadilly or Soho.

One of the most horrible eccentricities ever indulged in was that of John Donne, love poet and Dean of St. Paul's, who became, in his later years, so preoccupied with the thought of death, that for the last portrait to be painted of him, he insisted on standing in a coffin and wrapping himself in a white shroud.

Isaac Newton had a childish delight in blowing bubbles, and would do so for hours on end; Hugo Wolf, the German song-writer, would weep copiously when he played the piano; Schumann could never be persuaded to go beyond the second storey of a house, because of his fear of throwing himself out of the window; and Keats—though, perhaps, there is more wisdom in this man than anything else—was said to have peppered his tongue before drinking claret.

These, admittedly, are examples of freakish whims and caprices, rather than of madness or even of violent eccentricity. It is when we come to men like Edgar Allan Poe, out of whose disordered brain were created the 'Tales of Mystery and Imagination', that the real question of the associations between genius and insanity must be considered. Poe lived in a Stygian gloom of his own creating. He was a drunkard and a drug-addict, but the sheer, undiluted horror of some of his stories, their repulsive morbidity and their entire lack of normal values, is due neither to drugs nor drink. No man, unless partially insane, could have written such tales as those of his that deal with premature burial, and the fascination of the living for the dead.

John Clare, the rustic poet, whose works have, of recent years, enjoyed a certain popularity among literary scholars, spent the latter part of his life in a county asylum. His poems, some of which were written there, display a beauty of expression and a simplicity of feeling totally unallied with madness. Christopher Smart, too, who is remembered by his 'A Song to David', wrote his best work while in a mental home.

Paul Verlaine, the greatest lyric writer France has produced, who spent his last days in the most sordid poverty, wandering between hospitals and cafés, was one of the strangest men in the history of literature. The author of 'Flowers of Evil', Charles Baudelaire, the enfant terrible of French literature, led a mad, exotic life in India and Paris. His unwholesome, and yet brilliant, work was cried down by his contemporaries, and many of his poems were banned. He recoursed to opium; drank to excess; and died when aged 46, crippled with paralysis.

These are tragic figures, but, fortunately, many of the artistic eccentricities provide more laughter than tears. James Thomson, the author of the 'City of Dreadful Night', would spend a whole month in bed, although perfectly well, explaining his conduct by saying that it was quite futile getting out of bed when, at the end of the day, the only thing to do was to go back to it.

Eccentricity is not lacking among modern artists, as Miss Nina Hamnett, author of the banned book, 'Laughing Torso', is at pains to disclose. Thinking of all the tragedies and inconveniences that genius so often seems to carry with it, it is rather pleasant to be able to lie back and revel in ignorance. Who would be a genius after all?

TO PAMELA HANSFORD JOHNSON

From MSS correspondence in the Lockwood Memorial Library, New York. These criticisms of poems sent to the poet by Pamela Hansford Johnson during their now famous correspondence are omitted by Constantine FitzGibbon from his edition of the *Selected Letters* (Dent, 1966). The queried dates, however, are as suggested in that edition. Victor Neuberg was the editor of the 'Poets' Corner' of the *Sunday Referee*, the newspaper which effected the first volume-publication of both Dylan Thomas and Pamela Hansford Johnson. (See Constantine FitzGibbon, *The Life of Dylan Thomas*, Dent, 1965.)

And now I have eight poems of yours to do what I like with. And I am going to do what I like with them—criticize each in turn, not very minutely, for nothing short of fifty pages would allow it, but at least in some detail. Remember that nothing I say, Pamela, is for the sake of being smart, or to relieve any acid emotions I may have bottled up within me. I mean what I say and I mean it to help. Tell me if it is worth my while and your attention. If it is, then I will willingly, more than willingly, criticize in the same way every and any poem you have written.

SUNG IN A GARDEN AT NIGHTFALL

Delius should have written this instead of that extremely literary piece of music, Summer Night on the River. His music is a rebound, or, if you like, a second mood. First comes the idea of the creation, then the mental poem, then the composition of the music: a wrong method of approach. The nostalgia that runs through him like a vein drops 'jasmine-sweet' from your song. I'm glad that the colour of your poem book is green, the colour of youth when a minor heartbreak or the twiddly bit on an oboe is more effective than the sight of God or the feel of a surgical needle stuck into the tongue. And this is prejudiced,

I know. But I like the Garden Song, and if in places it is more intestinal than emotional, that is all to the good. And I confess to a slight retching at the phrases, 'Woven of saffron with a weft of blue', 'veiled with violet', 'The air is jasmine-sweet'. And I confess that the 'The lashes of the rose are seeled with dew' is very pretty. But the whole poem I should like to see upon the cover of a chocolate box; its flavours would mix well with the taste of coffee-centres and crème de menthe.

You have such a lot of the abilities that go towards making a *very* good poet that it seems a shame you don't take a firmer grasp on your susceptibilities to the easier emotions and images. The best advice in the world to a poetess is—Be a poet! Think of Mrs Browning and Emily Brontë. One wrote in quite a competent, female manner, the other androgynously. It's Neuberg's Heshe all over again, and Lawrence's Bull-cow.

Laze, if you will, in a gossamer evening, confiding with your summer lover (impersonal! impersonal!); think your thoughts, and weep over the jail-like attitude of the poplars. But make more out of that experience than a pretty patchwork of derivative images and puce emotions. The garden (God wot!) must fit the mind like a glove. You yourself make it hell or heaven. Nothing is beautiful unless you think it. Make of your Woodforde-Finden garden a valley Wagner might have been proud of, a little place Debussy would have lolled in, a rugby field for an infant Honneger. But don't take it as you find it. The garden was nothing. You descended on it like a bat from Chopin's belfry, and, lo, it was saccharine.

THE BÉGUINAGE

This is by far the best poem that I've seen of yours. It's hard to imagine that the same mind created this and the previous song. It is beautifully simple; two of the verses are perfect. The idea, the form and the expression, go hand-in-hand with a most satisfying delicacy. Out of more than fifty lines I can find only two that, in the slightest way, make discord. And those lines, oddly enough, are the two that begin the poem. I read them and expected Sousa orchestrated by Milhaud; I read on and got Mozart—a clumsy way of expressing my delight at forty-eight lines and my dislike of two.

Because I heap calumny on one poem, and immediately

cover the next poem in an appreciative pile of roses, don't imagine that I am so easily a victim to my emotions that my opinions are little meditated. I like to spit at what I consider bad or unworthy (and much of what you sent me is unworthy of you), and I like to enthuse over what I consider sincere, real, and valuable. Béguinage is all these three—not a Wordsworth model, or a chic adornment from the 'maison de Christina Rossetti', but an individual and highly successful production from the 'maison de P. H. J.'

POSSESSION

See criticism one, especially the comment upon the poet and the poetess. 'Possession' is essentially a woman's poem. 'Béguinage' belongs to neither sex. It is a poem, and that is all and enough. 'Possession' is, metrically, quite good, but it is aimed at too low a standard.

PROMENADE CONCERT

Like the little girl with the curl over her forehead, when you are good you are very, very good, and when you are bad you are horrid. But even in your least inspired moments—and Sir Henry, Wood by name and Wood by nature, seems to have had much effect upon your emotional and little upon your literary centres—good things rise out of the mediocrity as bubbles rise out of a marsh. There is, in the last stanza, an experience nakedly crystallized in a phrase:—

'clacking of applause without even the compliment
Of an age-old second of silence.'

And that one experience compensates for the hysteria of the preceding lines. Your sincerity is always undeniable, and your hell-paving intentions *do* come out in such phrases as

And the rivers of Eden
In the cold flute.

But these are pearls surrounded not only by the pig's ear but by the whole of his bristling body. The 'burning triumph', the 'stinging pain', 'the singing and weeping for glory', are an exhibition (not in the sense of the Steyning highbrow) of emotion rather than a condensing, a torrent rather than a regulated fall, and as such is strictly out of place in a poem. It is as though a painter had flung a great mass of colours on to his canvas, and said to his critics, 'This is a landscape, for these are the colours that I see on the hills. The placing, dividing, and forming of these colours I leave to you . . .'

And while the colours would be bound to have some emotional significance, they no more make a painting than they do a stick of rock.

TRIBUTE

A neat little advertisement, which might prove commercially saleable if 'Poetry' was changed to, say, 'Gibb's Dentifrice'. One can write of mysticism without being a mystic; Wordsworth proved that. One can write of poetry, too.

THROUGH THE NIGHT

Again, many of your merits and nearly all your faults come out in this. There is an obvious desire to say something and quite as obvious a reluctance to know what it is. There are *hints* of loveliness and the *statements* of verbosity. 'Drenched with rose', incidentally, is too reminiscent of de la Mare's 'Nod', in which the words, 'dim with rose . . . and drenched with dew' appear. My dislike of the word 'burgeon' is a purely personal one, as is my dislike of the word 'primrose'. Unfortunately both appear in this poem (I hope you notice that I have used the 'poem' and 'verse' discriminately in these tiny criticisms) to test my boast of unbias.

'Each window pane shoots fire' is too quick, too impetuous an image to be satisfactory. There, again, you put down the emotional essence of what you wanted to say before you put your literary intelligence to work. I don't know how long you spent over 'Through the Night', but twice the time would have doubled its value, making it a consistently *good* poem, for it is good (careful word) in patches now. The imperative lines are very effective. So is the climax, notwithstanding the 'mother-of-pearl into pallid primrose', the type of line I can only call too easily pretty.

UP TRAIN

Have I ever complimented you upon your command of conventional technique? If not, let me compliment you now, and also upon your ability to command the wider issues of form. 'Up Train' could have been written in no other way, the highest thing one can say of a technical experiment. 'Seed Nursery' has the simplicity of a nursery rhyme, set off by a remarkable diction, uninfluenced by any other diction I'm acquainted with.

> For the mad sweet-pea he rigs
> Pillaries of little twigs

gives me a most pleasant shock, a *physical* sensation. Few combinations of words have a physical effect upon me.

> And he sets between, for brushes,
> Meek and poodle-shaven bushes.

This, too, and many other lines in this lovely little poem— 'little' is the word, the littleness of a certain type of beauty, the littleness of ordered gardens, avenues, and a tidy sky—has the effect upon me of a curious and individual wine out of an old bottle marked with very colourful designs. And if these sentences are, in themselves, too rich and adjectival, blame your odd little muse and not me.

SYMPHONY FOR FULL ORCHESTRA

When I read this first I wasn't sure whether its peculiar form was entirely necessary. But slowly the voices of the orchestra insisted, and the long, drawn-out question of the woodwind became inevitable, until, at the end, I wondered why the whole question, 'O Star In The Dark' was not repeated. Perhaps, if I read it again, I will see a good reason why it should be as it is. The one, sudden entrance of the tympani is remarkably effective. I can hear the harps glissando-ing (can you spell it?) over their strange phrases, the sudden, unharplike sound of the word 'cerements', the sibilant and treble 'Cease!' as they begin. And now any doubts I entertained as to the inevitability of the orchestral form are vanquished. Inevitably the violins say, 'These are his hands on your breast', and as inevitably the brass cry out and say, 'Return, star-crossed, The bloodshot morn is nigh.'

There is, as there was in Béguinage, only one phrase I object to. '... Weave the straining clouds

Into maddened shrouds'

has too many words—and the wrong words—in it. The rhyme is a jingle. The adjectives add nothing. Polish up or remove that phrase, and I have no quarrel with the poem from beginning to end. In its limits, it is as lovely as anything I know.

And so what a strange, unequal selection of poems and verses you have sent me. You have sent me the sugariest custard, the cheapest port, and the most delicate white wine. I never remember before mixing my drinks so quickly, and, at the same time, so satisfyingly.

Never be pretty for the sake of being pretty. It's always in your power—and yours especially—to lift prettiness into your own sort of beauty. Whether it is the ultimate beauty I don't even care to guess; but much of it is what *I* understand to be beautiful. And that is all I can ever say.

(Late October 1933?)

If you like, pay little attention to the following criticisms of your poems, for they are based, as what I write is based, on my own peculiar standards, which may be the standards of a theorising failure and a bilious little crank.

I now stop turning over the dirty pages of my soul, lick my pencil, wipe my cold-filled nose, light a cigarette, and write.

SOME FRANK CRITICISM
TWENTY TO TWELVE

Your ability to romanticize an atmosphere and to catch, with some considerable skill, the visual essences of a scene, is well displayed in this. But the whole thing is very slight, and would please the Refereaders more than it does me. It hangs between verse and poetry, and can either be called frail poetry or strong verse. I would prefer to call it the latter; it is a talented piece of versifying, facile, ornamental, and hung about with skilful images. But it lacks subtlety; the images, striking as they are,

are too patently obvious for the entire effect to stir much more than one's visual senses. There is no one line I can condemn; the thing is perfect, too perfect. This is more of an achievement than many other poems of yours, but the achievement is very limited. This is to me, the *wrong* direction. It is difficult to explain, in a short note, where the wrongness lies, but I do hope I have made myself clear. It has, apparently, nearly everything a poem needs—an experience, a fairly original diction, and an emotive appeal. Analysed more closely, it has nothing. You haven't given yourself enough to contend with. Knowing your own skill, you pick on something very easy to do, and do it, of course, skilfully and perfectly. Is it worth doing?

FEBRUARY

The same thing applies. Are you going to be content with a narrow achievement or a wide promise? This, again, is pretty, skilful, and visual. And, I personally, don't care a damn for prettiness or skill, while the putting down of what the eyes have seen (plus a few literary affectations and one or two unusual literary words) has very little to do with poetry. Unless the spirit illuminates what the eyes have mirrored, then all the paraphernalia of the winter scene is as valueless as an Academy picture of Balmoral Castle.

REQUIEM FOR SPRING

The same criticism applies, with the exception that in this even the skill is a little bowed at the knees.

Of roses she bestows a lavish spate
The hedgerows and the garden to bedizen

is as bad as anything the Poet's Corner has ever printed. Indeed, every verse is. I'm glad you didn't send it for my benefit. And God help Neuberg's taste. What was the matter with you when you wrote this?

RETROSPECT

All your skill and command of words, added, as you explain, to the cries of a halfmended (or is it fully mended?) heartbreak, make this a moderately good poem, with one or two touches of superlatively good writing. It is narrow, again, but its limits are the essential limits of the subject you impose on yourself.

'Blown into dust upon the morning sun' is an inevitably beautiful line, but the extraction of all the lovely phrases would mean quoting *nearly* every word. The pause in the last line is most effective.

Not perfect but promising. And if you've read all I've written before (a sudden terrible thought that you show my letters to your mother), you'll know how complimentary this is.

One thing: phrases such as 'the mirage of eternity' are meaningless unless you qualify them.

BLACK MASS

No, I can't like it. I've tried very hard, but just as I'm beginning to say to myself, 'Oh well, this is quite all right', along comes a revoltingly saccharine line, or some coy, girlish sentiment, or a piece of very ordinary clumsiness.

> The lilies, the innocent lilies, are troubled,
> The trees rub their eyes awake,
> And the mice, the little mice that nibble the grasses,
> Crouch in the stones; their noses shiver with fear.

This is very pleasant; trivial, no doubt, but charmingly done; any moment a selfconscious Pan might come around the corner. Instead, that damned chorus starts again with all their 'silvered intaglio, livid seraglio' business. Occasionally I see something I like—rivers bisecting faces, 'they are surrounding the hills in a ring' (nice and simple), but far more often I see things that sicken me, the jimjackery and jugglebuggery of the *bad* and *pretentious* versifier. If you *were* bad and pretentious I wouldn't mind, but, as I've repeated so many times, you have nearly everything that contributes towards the make-up of an individual, original, and satisfying poet. If I didn't like you I wouldn't waste ten seconds over the Black Mass. I don't mean to be cruel, but there it is. I see, even in this *very* bad effort, the mentality that produced the Symphonic poem. But in this case you let your taste go down into the sugary vaults. Take a firm grip, for the lord's sake, on your treacherous aptitudes for prettiness, pretty chaos and word spinning.

THE MORNING SUN

By far the most curious poem you have sent me, this moves in a circle of words and feeling, disregarding itself, and falling, inevitably, into its own pattern. Even the touches I do not like do not fail in the general content, but only to the critical eye and ear that, after the first unqualifying response, pursue the ghosts of syllables into the deadends of the purist lanes. Re-reading what I have written I understand very little of it. The fault, dear Pamela, lies in your stars. Your stars are not mine; they twinkle in a different heaven, higher or lower than mine I cannot tell. Perhaps it would be as well if I contented myself with saying of this very individual poem, 'I understand and appreciate', without bothering to go into the details of appreciation. But I cannot do that; I want you to go on writing like this, never whoreing yourself to the fingers of prettiness or the charms of a cheap simile.

All your creeds of simplicity, that surely must comply with the dictates of the ballad form rather than with the long, spongy lines of the sonnet, are obeyed. Indeed, the poem opens on a ballad note, on a naïve note thrilling with innumerable and subtle suggestions. The visual element is, again, very strong—I positively can see you, poor stranger in yourself, walking along the crowded pavements and gazing wonderingly down on your 'busy' hips (the perfect adjective)—but, this time, justifiably so. The language is economical and true, with a few exceptions, and the experience *is* a poetical one, and not merely the emotions of a self-confessed romanticist or the romances of a self-denied sentimentalist.

Here are the exceptions: 'I think of sunlight and a pile of books'. Many bad poems, imitative of Rupert Brooke's bad poem, 'The Great Lover', include a catalogue of personal likes such as, 'Green apples in the morning sun', 'The kiss of rain upon the rose', and, inevitably, the more overpoweringly senti-mental like—more overpowering because of its reversed senti-mentality—'rough blankets on the skin' or 'the smell of tweeds'. The line of yours could easily be included in such a feminine catalogue. It is too sweet, and reminds me too much of Percy Lubbock's 'Earlham'. Alter it.

'OF BROOKS THAT GARGLE'

The associations are absurd, and the sound is ugly. You have said the same of phrases in *my* poems, but this is, strictly, such a *beautiful* thing that the intrusion of one discordant line must not spoil it.

'*will be forgotten as a twisted dream*'. This adjective is wrong. You want a less sophisticated adjective, such as 'wicked' or even 'ugly', although I am not suggesting these. You will be able to find a better and more harmonious one. For the rest I have no complaints.

> I feel the stocking pulling at my leg,
> And there is not a stranger in myself

is severely and *mystically* physical, though many people won't see it. Write like this always, and I shan't grumble.

'Never strain after prettiness', my first injunction, is now supplemented by, 'Never use your skill for the sake of skilfulness', and 'Be yourself in your poetry as you are in your letters'. Morning Sun could have been written by no-one but yourself. If you like, I will write more about this poem in my next letter. I have crowds of things to say about it, and some of what I say *may* help you.

(11 November 1933)

THREE POEMS

I don't honestly feel disposed to throw you a bone for your three most recent poems; you certainly deserve a whole puppy biscuit for the sixteen lines of 'Quest', and also, perhaps, a little bit of puppy food for the 'Motorists'. But you don't get a single mouthful for 'December Trees'.

QUEST

This is a very slight thing but quite successful in its limits, and the last five lines are attractive *because* of their slightness and simplicity. 'Weeps, just because of it', a rather whimsy line, might be improved by the deletion of the comma which makes, to me, a quite unessential pause. I haven't decided yet about the adjective 'unquiet'. As a rule I dislike such negative words, except in very especial instances. If a thing is not quiet there is no real need to say that it is not; it is much better to say what it is. 'Unquiet' doesn't *qualify* the mouse; I've told you of my belief as the poetical function of the adjective before, haven't I? —'unquiet' doesn't add anything to the mouse. The thing to remember is that everyone has his different associations for every word; one person may, for some Freudian reason, associate 'mouse' with horrors and death's heads, another with a certain soft material or colour. So the poet who is going to put an adjective before 'mouse' must say to himself: I have two alternatives; either I can create such a tremendous and universal adjective that it will *embrace* every association built around the word—that is, it must be an adjective that complies with all the associations from horror to colour; or I must create an adjective that will *break down* all associations, and make the 'mouse' a new thing with new associations. Does 'unquiet' satisfy either of those tests? I don't know. I rather think, despite my theories, that it is a very effective word. It must be one of those especial instances where such a negation can be used.

THE MOTORISTS

This is much the sort of thing that another (no, no, please, I don't mean that) of Neuberg's animals produces—one Harry Hodgkinson by name. The last four lines are, unfortunately, for they are good, spoilt for me by the fact that I know a very vulgar schoolboy poem in the same metre. The poem (the 'Motorists', not 'Eskimo Nell') is bright and refreshing, but the sort of cheery poetry that makes me even more depressed than the 'City of Dreadful Night'. That, again, is personal. As a rule I try to criticize your poems from a *pure* poetical standpoint, but various things prevent me from doing it with this. And down comes my omnipotent criticship with a bump. 'And scratch her great, brown face' is clumsy. Why the two bumpy little adjectives? Go on, tell me it's intentional.

DECEMBER TREES

Just what you shouldn't write. Leave these 'Notes from a Rambler's LogBook' to other and far less talented young women. It's the easiest and least valuable form of valueless impressionism.

> December trees—
> Brown mists above the fields

is the sort of opening one comes across on nearly every other page of 'The Best (or Worst) Poems of the Year', which is a collection of shattered pieces of sentimental romanticism swept up by that literary charwoman, Mr Thomas Moult.

> October fields—
> A breath of wind about the sedge,
> A speckled rabbit in a hedge,
> And cold white snow.

No, girl, no. This is terribly unworthy of you. Develop—and you can develop at a tremendous speed—along the lines of 'Quest' and 'I feel I am a stranger', that lovely poem that does and always will remain in my memory. Write out of yourself, and leave the hedgerows and the *visual* aspects of the country-side. And another thing: don't be afraid, at this stage of your development, to intellectualise more. Intellect alone never makes good poetry. You have the essential attributes of poetry, so can do no harm to yourself by letting your intellect have, now, a certain amount of freedom.

(Late 1933)

Your poems are changing, and for the better. The change, not the fulfilment, is quite evident in the poem you sent me. 'Pinguid' *is* a lovely word, but it is also an affected word. It means fat, doesn't it, and is an obvious Latinization. Your first line would be vastly improved if you changed it to its English equivalent. Or even said, 'A gray, old satyr, lying in the shade'. Anything like that, the more naive the better. I see that the females who now adorn your poems are a very athletic lot. One woman would keep leaping on to vines (probably an alcoholic complex), and now you have a girl who leaps about so indiscriminately that she is called the 'leaping' girl and left at that. I'm not laughing at this sudden introduction of the sporting element. Far from it. I'm just writing a lot of nonsense while I

try to define my reactions to the 'Poem' as a whole. The motif—
let me have my jargon—is good, and 'curling' into the womb is
just the sort of juicy anatomical conceit I love. I can't like the
second line of the last stanza. I fail to see *why* she should bite
her lip, or change colour like a piece of litmus paper. She should
have been more subtle in her—what is it?—her [disg]loathing,
though neither that nor the crossed-off word are the ones I
mean. She needn't have gone to the trouble of gnawing her
own anatomy. The old boy, pinguid as ever, could merely have
looked into her eyes, and seen there, hidden deeply away, the
reason for him letting her go. Which would be much better
psychologically, and would probably result in a better poetical
line.

The two prose-poems (I'll allow you that) are very uneven.
Much of the writing is, for you, almost criminally wrong, being
just what you can do so well but shouldn't. You can lavish the
best lavishers in the country off their spates when you want to.
But don't you dare do it. But what the hell's the good of me
talking if you listen with one ear and with the other catch the
modulations of the bagpipe and the rippling rill? Piece One is
remarkable for the number of entirely meaningless and
affected words you have managed to drag in. 'Dulcimer',
'Drumdeep', 'Cohorts', and 'Silken, Shadowy Girls'. All the
damned abracadabra of the Poet's Corner, and as gutless as a
filleted herring. What does it mean, anyway, this coy questioning of the heart (a few centuries ago it would have been the
liver, a far better emotional prophet) as to whether you shall,
or shall not, do a bit of 'arping? This asking your heart to
browse, like a cow, in the lilies? This semi-devotional-mystical
voodoo of Saint John and the Seven Candlesticks? What does it
mean: I don't want a message; I believe that poetry can have
only one message. My latest definition of poetry is 'The expression of the unchanging spirit in the changing flesh' (I may have
told it to you before). But I want something more than this
insipid uncertainty, this amorous insistence on the 'silk' in
girls, this squeaking of 'dulcimers' when the dulcimer is an out-
dated and useless thing. In this Piece you adopt the same
attitude that makes a person call a poet a 'troubador'. Why
'cohorts'? Ah I know the reason. 'Cohorts' is a pretty word,
with a lot of nice, dim, tapestry associations. But, my dear, you

aren't doing a piece of embroidery. You're writing a poem. And
the whole trouble is, of course, that you aren't. These Pieces
should never have been straggled out as prose. You should have
written them in metre, and they would have been bloody still.

I will knock this romanticist warbling of yours out of your
head. I've got a lot to say to you, but I'll wait till I *see* you. Then
I can tell you really what I mean. 'The blood-wet rags of the
beggar' is good, and so are little patches—I keep coming back,
however unconsciously, to embroidery images—in 'Fear',
which is, as a whole, almost worse. One of my troubles in
slating these is my conscious feeling that the *emotion* in both *is*
worth expressing. But, far from there being too little, there is
too much 'peace in your pen'. It flows—that's the word—far
too quickly and fluidly.

(28 March 1934?)

Your poem is good, and promising. It is careful, well modulated, and, fortunately, neither too sweet nor too simple. I don't
know about the sixth line of the first verse, which sounds something like the opening line in a London Mercury sonnet. And
the seventh and eighth line of the second verse are quite bad.
The poem is intelligent, and has many beautiful phrases. 'The
blood was love'. 'The funnel of the tempers'. The lost Atlantis
line is a successful surprise. On the whole, it's one of your best
poems. Obviously much care has been taken with it, and if
these remarks do sound unnaturally guarded it is because your
poetry is changing so definitely in attitude, and is becoming so
much more intense and muscular, that I am frightened to say
much for fear of interrupting its progress. I always knew you
had a splendid poetry in you; now it's forming itself. My
influences, obvious mainly in lines five, ten, and thirteen, and,
perhaps, in the construction of a few other phrases, will drop
away and leave your verse naked and itself. Progress from this,
but don't, as in the lines of the 'stucco wall' and the 'line of
lamplight', sink to an easy impressionist objectiveness. Both
these lines could have appeared in Rupert Brooke's 'Great
Lover' catalogue, and have no place in a poem such as this. Not
much of a comment on the poem, I'm afraid. But what it
promises is so good that I daren't say anything more. Go on,
work on from this. Condense even more. Oh, I forgot—line

TO PAMELA HANSFORD JOHNSON

nine is bad, too. Another item in the Rupert catalogue. The rest—too good for me to spoil, and an incalculable improvement on nearly all that is printed in 'Symphony' . . .

I have just finished a review for the Adelphi. God, some tripe is published. Out of seven books sent by Rees only two are worth anything. The other five are unbelievably bad. Excerpt from 'The Selected Poems of Charles King':

> Thou camest from the Paradise of Love,
> A fondling in the dew-drops, out of Time,
> When far in Being's arcane Hesperid-grove
> Strayed Mona Lisa with her Prince of Rhyme.

Excerpt from Frank Kendon's 'Tristram':

> The thirsty greyhound drew his leash
> Tighter about Sir Tristram's wrist;
> He heard a noise of rising water:
> The dog should wet its thirst, at least.

Excerpt from 'Singing Waters' by Ian Dall:

> As might a butterfly when first
> It from the dark cocoon does burst
> He rises from the rippled ring
> To joy of rhythmic uttering.

And a poem by Sydney Salt, one of the highbrows of Majorca:

> Seeing Goya.
>
> Goya shot a few bullets through the sky.
> So did Dostoevsky—who else?
> Hungry men these, who knew the meaning of lean.

What a life is the life of a hack reviewer. Thank God the others, William Soutar and William Montgomerie (Squared Circle) are very traditional and very competent. Sydney is nuts.

(Week of 5 July 1934)

SPAJMA AND SALNADY: OR WHO SHOT THE EMU? A ONE ACT PLAY NEVER TO BE PRESENTED

From MSS in the Lockwood Memorial Library, New York. This was sent as a joke to Pamela Hansford Johnson early in 1934. It is omitted from FitzGibbon's edition of the *Selected Letters*. A note at the head of the MS explains the names of the hero and heroine as anagrams on those of the poet and his correspondent.

SCENE ONE

(The scene is set in a large hall, curtained in red and puce; there are scarlet bananas painted all over the ceiling, and the skins of dead lepers cover the floor; all the doors are the wrong way up and have no knobs, an oversight made up for by the fact that there are knobs on nearly everything else; in the corners can be seen the garrotted bodies of old herbalists, the left arms of postmen, and the complete works of Galsworthy. When the curtain rises, the scene is in darkness. After the third hour of darkness, a very small voice is heard saying, 'For Christ's sake put on the light, Albert.' The lights go up, and the Spirit of Poetry—a stout, middle-aged woman clad in a fireman's costume—is seen to be brooding in the middle of the stage.)

SPIRIT OF POETRY: Life is like that; it always reminds me of Scarlatti, for fugue people know how to enjoy it. How can *I* be possibly expected to be un-miserable when, like a professed midwife or a smalltown whoremaster, I am knocked and called up at all hours of the day and night? Day after day, week after week, pale young people come up to me, and, with hardly a smile or a goodmorning, ask for a quick half pound of inspiration all about pimps and gasworks. And

140

probably at that very moment I am making up a private verse of my own concerning the beauty of the gum-trees in Radnorshire. But of course I always oblige 'em; I give them their half pound, with a couple of drains thrown in, and then . . .

(A Startled Young Poet with peas in his hair suddenly thrusts his head round one of the curtains.)

STARTLED YOUNG POET: Give me a rhyme for 'pimp', quick.

SPIRIT OF POETRY: 'Limp', you bloody fool.

(The S.Y.P. cackles and retires).

There you are, you see what I was telling you. It's like that all day. And the things I've got to provide: everything from traction-engines for the Realists to anemones for the Kiplings or Kiplets. Oh, why wasn't I the Spirit of Carpentry; carpenters need such small vocabularies.

(Enter a Pale Realist in spats.)

PALE REALIST: Quick, give me a rhyme for 'gasworks'.

SPIRIT OF POETRY: I can't, there isn't one.

PALE REALIST: Oh, yes there is.

SPIRIT OF POETRY: Oh, no there isn't.

PALE REALIST: Oh, yes there is.

(This argument would go on for some considerable time, but it is broken by the entrance of Spajma Oh-no-nel, the poetess; bearing her famous torso proudly in front of her—a couple of very old publishers are hiding in it, by the way—she steps between the combatants.)

SPAJMA: Stop!

(They stop.)

SPIRIT OF POETRY: Oh Gawd, you here again?

(The Pale Realist sees her, makes a noise in his teeth, and vanishes.)

SPAJMA: I want half a pound of the usual, please.

SPIRIT OF POETRY: All right, all right, don't hurry me. Where's the other swine?

SPAJMA: What other swine?

SPIRIT OF POETRY: You know.

SPAJMA: Oh, Salnady Moth, you mean?

SPIRIT OF POETRY: Of course that's who I mean. Where is
he? I gave him a stanza too much yesterday, and the day
before he stole a short story when I wasn't looking. You can't
trust those Metaphysicians; they'd steal the eggstains from
the corners of your mouth. What did you say you wanted?

SPAJMA: Half a pound of the usual, please, and a rhyme for
'navel'.

SPIRIT OF POETRY: 'Navel'? No, no, you don't mean
'navel' my dear; that's the wrong word for your school; you
probably mean 'grovel'.

SPAJMA: No I don't; 'navel' I want; and tomorrow I'll want
six 'bellies' and a 'senna-pod'.

SPIRIT OF POETRY: I knew it; it's that dreadful Moth
creature; he's corrupting you.

(Enter Salnady Moth, with a leer.)

SALNADY: Good morning. A quick womb, please, two milks,
a hangman, a dash of sleep and a pint of wax.

(With a scream, the poor Spirit makes her exit, doubtlessly
going in the direction of the Metaphysical Stores. Our hero and
heroine are left alone.)

SALNADY: Nice weather we're having. What have you been
doing lately?

SPAJMA: I've been to see John Barrymore on the films. Don't
you love his moustache?

SALNADY: I'm afraid I very rarely go to the pictures. The
vast majority of films is atrociously bad, but that is not the
reason which prevents me from going. My diurnal round—
with which, from our last conversation, you are acquainted—
allows little time for me to sit, holding a greasy hand in mine,
to swoon before the magnified image of a platinum blonde, or
to wonder how much worse that mountebank of an actor,
John Barrymore, can possibly be in his next film. A good
description of him is: a bunch of mannerisms and a profile.
Among the few films I have enjoyed are: the Cabinet of Dr
Caligari, Atalanta, Student of Prague, Edge of the World,
Vaudeville, Waxworks, the Street, M, and Blue Angel (all
German); Sur les Toits de Paris; Potemkin (Russian); The
Gold Rush, the Three Little Pigs, and the Marx Brothers

comedies (American). The 'Bill of Divorcement' was not a film at all, but a screened play very badly and very theatrically acted, with the exception of the girl; the plot was disastrously altered, and the introduction of that wretched 'unfinished sonata' reached the depths of bathos.

SPAJMA : Don't you like Norma Shearer, Lionel Barrymore, Clark Gable, George Raft, Joan Crawford, Uncle Tom Navarro and all?

SALNADY : No. I like abstruse poetry, symbolical fiction, discordant music, and beer. Oh, yes, I like you, too, by the way.

SPAJMA : (coyly) Wait till you know me proper, flesh and all.

SALNADY : Don't be pornographic. I said I like you, and I do. When I know you better I shall like you better. I know. It's I'm the trouble. There's the great possibility, or even probability, that you won't like me at all.

SPAJMA : I agree. But tell me, who was that burner of boats who has been playing ducks and drakes with the lily of my reputation?

SALNADY : To translate: you mean who was it who said that he had met you and did not like you?

SPAJMA : Yes.

SALNADY : It was Arty Young Person who met you—only for an hour or two—in Steyning, where, in the company of a tall thing and a limping girl, he had come to have tea and argue with Victor Neuberg. You were there, so he tells me, lying in a hammock or some such thing and looking very bored at his conversational efforts. Neuberg showed him your poems, and he did not like them. In his own words 'she' (you) 'had a nice body but a bloody brain'. He made another couple of rude remarks, too, but I'm too much of a gentleman to repeat them. Beneath my black shirt beats a white heart.

SPAJMA : And that's all.

SALNADY : That is all. I think I'm Pretty Decent to tell you. I could have kept you curious for ages. But then the incident is very little in itself. He liked what he saw of the body but didn't like what he saw of the mind; I like what I've seen of the mind and haven't seen any of the body. But I like both.

SPAJMA : I hated him, anyway. Or didn't I?

(At this enigmatic point, the two agèd publishers leap out of

Spajma's capacious torso where they have been hiding and eavesdropping—eavesdropping in the torsoes of lady poets is still, incidentally, a much practised recreation in many parts of Shropshire—and execute a nimble dance around the handsome, if pygmy, couple.)

FIRST PUBLISHER: I wanted to publish your book but I didn't like the title.

SECOND PUBLISHER: I wanted to publish your book but the title gave me the pip.

SALNADY: What was the title?

BOTH PUBLISHERS: Symphony for Full Orchestra . . .

(And with a howl they vanish under one another's beards.)

SPAJMA: This comes as a surprise to me. Don't *you* like the title?

SALNADY: Not I. I like it less than 'Dayspring'. You won't take offence, I know, when I tell you what impression such a title might give one. It sounds rather presumptuous, I'm afraid, as if your undoubted talents had reached their full maturity. If I were a cynical reviewer, I might be tempted to say: 'Miss Johnson is a gifted composer—for the piccolo.' You don't mind my saying I don't like the title, do you? I'd much prefer just 'Poems' or 'Thirty Poems' or even 'First Poems'. Still, I am very much looking forward to my signed Presentation Copy from the author.

(For the first time Spajma perceives that her companion is walking—though, of course, he is not walking at the moment—with a hobble and a stick.)

SPAJMA: (with interest) Why are you limping?

SALNADY: I have sprained my ankle, and very painful it is, too. It happened like this: (Spajma looks very bored, but he continues) On Sunday nights it is my custom to go to my Mermaid hotel—you can't have an official drink in Wales on a Sunday, of course—creep up the stairs and into the manageress's room where, in the company of the manageress herself—a stout, charming, middle-aged girl with red hair and a thirst—a dim barmaid, my dress-designing toper, I consume too much out of too many bottles, argue on obscure religious points, and listen to a gramophone. Last Sunday I

stayed longer than usual, and, in attempting to go downstairs to the bar, slipped and fell a considerable way. My
ankle went up like a balloon and I retired to bed, the
manageress's bandages, sympathetic stories from the toper,
and more beer. There was slight annoyance when I arrived
home in time for dinner the next day. The untidiness of my
speech is due to the fact that I am still in great pain.

SPAJMA: There's a pity, you sot. But you're too young for all
this lordishness, aren't you? You probably think it's very
smart and wicked of you. It's just childish.

SALNADY: Possibly. But it must be drink or drug, you know.

SPAJMA: Yah! Haven't you any ambitions?

SALNADY: (with a subtle leer) Yes, to learn German.

(This remark is greeted with derisive laughter from the 147
dumb Jews who have just come in.)

SPAJMA: No, real ambitions, not laughable ones like that.

SALNADY: That was real. But I should like to see a crippled
yoddler throwing almanacks from the top of the Matterhorn;
I should like to see a Bulgarian spy eat spinach with a violin
bow; I should like to see a bankrupt teacher of eurhythmics
stealing the dental plate from a Yukon trapper; I should like
to stand on an ice-floe and teach Rameau to a class of conies;
and I should like to learn German.

SPAJMA: And you think you're funny.

(She joins in the general Jewish laughter and spits elegantly
at the approaching figure of the Spirit of Poetry.)

SPIRIT OF POETRY: It's no good; I've run out of all you
want. Mr Moth, you have used up all the available milk,
wombs, wax, hangmen, and sleep. Miss Oh-no-nel, there's
none of your usual left: you've used it all up, all your bliss
and rowan hedges, your half-forgotten loves and tired trees,
your absent Pucks, your Titania-lidded roses.

SPAJMA AND SALNADY: Then what on earth are we to do?

SPIRIT OF POETRY: Nothing on earth, my children. Neither
in hangmen nor roses will you find what you want. You must
go and look far away. Both of you are too limited.

SALNADY: Oh, but I wrote an awfully good story called 'The
Tree'.

SPAJMA: Well, I liked it anyway, though other people

probably won't. And I wrote two awfully good poems; one was called 'Phoenix', and I didn't have a title for the other one.

SALNADY: Yes, I liked them. But I'll tell you all about them in detail the next time we meet.

SPIRIT OF POETRY: Yes, and this mutual admiration pleases *me* very much. But there's nothing left of your old stuff, and what there is is in the bargain basement of the Metaphysical Stores. This hall is very big, but it becomes very stuffy at times. And I don't like the way these 147 dumb Jews keep popping in and out.

SPAJMA: Who are they?

SPIRIT OF POETRY: Oh, they are the Philistines of the world; they always hang around the doors of this building. When anybody asks me for something particularly absurd or eccentric, or when the same person asks me for the same things all the time, or when anybody makes a more than usually silly remark, they all charge in and jeer. They're probably not so dumb as we think. Now don't hang about here any more, there's good children. Go away, it's much bigger and brighter outside. Parnassus—and pardon the cliché, me dears—is always outside; you know that don't you? Out you go, and do a bit of climbing.

(The Startled Young Poet, the Pale Realist, and many thousands of young women in hand painted sandals suddenly burst through the door and shout at the Spirit. Spajma and Salnady go out together. The Jews see them go, but for once they do not jeer.)

SCENE TWO

(The scene is changed. The hall has given place to a great stretch of mountains, and the ceiling to the stretch of a mad and star-covered sky. It is dark. Spajma and Salnady are standing motionless upon the lowland, looking up at the lean tops of the mountains. Though it is too dark to see their faces, we know that they are despairing. Though their dark bodies are faded into the dark body of the night, we know that they are weak and tired. There are voices heard or there are no voices heard. It might be the silence that speaks, or the speakers themselves may be silent. But we who stand at a great distance hear those voices say: 'What a little way you have come and yet how tired you are. Joseph leading the Virgin on an ass's back was no tireder than you.' We hear:)

FIRST MOUNTAIN: I am the mountain at the beginning, a suffering of a hill. Milk runs over me. There is blood in my hands. You cannot help but climb me.

(And we do not know whether the sighing is the sighing of Spajma and Salnady as they climb up the milky rocks, or the suffering sighing of the hill. We hear:)

SECOND MOUNTAIN: I am a blind, hot hill, hungry for the food of the stars, to whom this musical world around me is as white and as kind as a breast. You cannot help but climb me.

SALNADY: Unmilk me of this mothering hill.

SECOND MOUNTAIN: Take my blind life. Rebel and rabble, take the wind of my food, let it blow in your spaces.

A GREAT VOICE: There is a hole in space.

(And all the time we see Salnady's darkness, we see the darkness of Spajma, climbing the sides of the rocks. We hear:)

THIRD MOUNTAIN: I am a happy hill. (We see a contented lightning light him up like a match. We hear:) There is laughter in my green, there are sheep on my sides, there is piping in my shades. (And all the hills echo. We see that the sky is an old man. We hear:) You cannot help but climb me.

FOURTH MOUNTAIN: I am a strange, new hill, blacker and whiter than all the boys' bones under the sea, than all the girls' bones in their unhallowed acres. (The old man has gone, and the sky is naked. She has unbuttoned her stars. We see the faces in the flesh of her breasts. We hear the music in the chiming of her wrists and the stream of her tickling hair. We hear:) Climb me, you cannot help but climb me. I burn like a fat in the fire, I lie cool like a nail in the grass. I am what you will have me, weak or strong, light or dark, warm as ice, cold as flame. I burn, I burn. When you leave me, I go out. You cannot help but climb me.

(We see Salnady's brightness, the lightness of Spajma, illu-minated against the hill. There are colours on the nakedness of the sky. Now the sky is a woman, now the sky is a man, unbuttoned of the stars. He is hot, she is cold, she is hot, he is cold. He wrinkles and ages, she is younger than her blood, he is an infant, she is a mother. We hear:)

SPAJMA AND SALNADY: Where are the others, the other climbers?

A GREAT VOICE: For one there is no other. There are no others. There is a hole in space.

(We see the ghosts at the lever of the curtains. We expect to see the climbers climb higher and higher as the invisible hands bring down the sky. But they are motionless. There is another scene. There is an interval, stranger than the play itself. We go out and have a drink in the interval, and are served by young and old. There is a star in our cup. And, drinking, we remember how our two players had been left, low on the fringes of the fourth mountain, looking up at a sky, looking down at a sky. 'Tell us', we ask a critic, 'What is the dramatist going to do with Spajma? Will they move, will they stay, one move one stay?' But he cannot tell us, the interval is long, and the star has the tail of a comet hanging like the wick of a witch's candle over our one cup.)

ANSWERS TO AN ENQUIRY

From *New Verse*, no. 11 (October 1934), pp. 8–9.

I. DO YOU INTEND YOUR POETRY TO BE USEFUL TO YOURSELF OR OTHERS?

To both. Poetry is the rhythmic, inevitably narrative, movement from an overclothed blindness to a naked vision that depends, in its intensity on the strength of the labour put into the creation of the poetry. My poetry is, or should be, useful to me for one reason: it is the record of my individual struggle from darkness towards some measure of light, and what of the individual struggle is still to come benefits by the sight and knowledge of the faults and fewer merits in that concrete record. My poetry is, or should be, useful to others for its individual recording of that same struggle with which they are necessarily acquainted.

2. DO YOU THINK THERE CAN NOW BE A USE FOR NARRATIVE POETRY?

Yes. Narrative is essential. Much of the flat, abstract poetry of the present has no narrative movement, no movement at all, and is consequently dead. There must be a progressive line, or theme, of movement in every poem. The more subjective a poem, the clearer the narrative line. Narrative, in its widest sense, satisfies what Eliot, talking of 'meaning', calls 'one habit of the reader'. Let the narrative take that one logical habit of the reader along with its movement, and the essence of the poem will do its work on him.

3. DO YOU WAIT FOR A SPONTANEOUS IMPULSE BEFORE
WRITING A POEM; IF SO, IS THIS IMPULSE VERBAL
OR VISUAL?

No. The writing of a poem is, to me, the physical and
mental task of constructing a formally watertight compart-
ment of words, preferably with a main moving column (i.e.,
narrative) to hold a little of the real causes and forces of the
creative brain and body. The causes and forces are always
there, and always need a concrete expression. To me, the
poetical 'impulse' or 'inspiration' is only the sudden, and
generally physical, coming of energy to the constructional,
craftsman ability. The laziest workman receives the fewest
impulses. And vice versa.

4. HAVE YOU BEEN INFLUENCED BY FREUD AND HOW
DO YOU REGARD HIM?

Yes. Whatever is hidden should be made naked. To be
stripped of darkness is to be clean, to strip of darkness is to
make clean. Poetry, recording the stripping of the individual
darkness, must inevitably, cast light upon what has been
hidden for too long, and, by so doing, make clean the naked
exposure. Freud cast light on a little of the darkness he had
exposed. Benefiting by the sight of the light and the knowledge of the hidden nakedness, poetry must drag further into
the clean nakedness of light more even of the hidden causes
than Freud could realise.

5. DO YOU TAKE YOUR STAND WITH ANY POLITICAL OR
POLITICO-ECONOMIC PARTY OR CREED?

I take my stand with any revolutionary body that asserts
it to be the right of all men to share, equally and impartially,
every production of man from man and from the sources of
production at man's disposal, for only through such an
essentially revolutionary body can there be the possibility of
a communal art.

6. AS A POET WHAT DISTINGUISHES YOU, DO YOU
THINK, FROM AN ORDINARY MAN?

Only the use of the medium of poetry to express the
causes and forces which are the same in all men.

THE COST OF LETTERS

From *Horizon*, vol. 14, no. 81 (September 1946), pp. 173–5.

1. HOW MUCH DO YOU THINK A WRITER NEEDS TO LIVE ON?

He needs as much money as he wants to spend. It is after his housing, his feeding, his warming, his clothing, the nursing of his children, etc., have been seen to—and these should be seen to by the State—that he really needs money to spend on all the luxurious necessities. Or, it is then that he doesn't need money because he can do without those necessary luxuries. How much money depends, quite obviously, on how much he wants to buy. I *want* a lot, but whether I *need* what I want is another question.

2. DO YOU THINK A SERIOUS WRITER CAN EARN THIS SUM BY HIS WRITING, AND IF SO, HOW?

A serious writer (I suppose by this you mean a good writer, who might be comic) can earn enough money by writing seriously, or comically, if his appetites, social and sensual, are very small. If those appetites are big or biggish, he cannot earn, by writing what he wishes to write, enough to satisfy them. So he has to earn money in another way: by writing what he doesn't want to write, or by having quite another job.

3. IF NOT, WHAT DO YOU THINK IS THE SUITABLE SECOND OCCUPATION FOR HIM?

It's no good I suppose, saying that I know a couple of good writers who are happy writing, for a living, what they don't particularly want to write, and also a few good writers who are happy (always qualified by words I'm not going to use now) being bank clerks, Civil Servants, etc. I can't say how a writer can make money most suitably. It depends on how much money he wants and on how much he wants it and on what he is willing to do to get it. I myself get about a quarter of the money I want by writing what I don't want to write and at the same time trying to, and often succeeding in, enjoying it. Shadily living by one's literary wits is as good a way of making too little money as any other, so long as, all the time you are writing B.B.C. and film-scripts, reviews, etc., you aren't thinking, sincerely, that this work is depriving the world of a great poem or a great story. Great, or at any rate very good, poems and stories do get written in spite of the fact that the writers of them spend much of their waking time doing entirely different things. And even a poet like Yeats, who was made by patronage financially safe so that he need not write and think nothing but poetry, *had*, voluntarily, to give himself a secondary job: that of philosopher, mystic, crank, quack.

4. DO YOU THINK LITERATURE SUFFERS FROM THE DIVERSION OF A WRITER'S ENERGY INTO OTHER EMPLOYMENTS OR IS IT ENRICHED BY IT?

No, to both questions. It neither suffers nor is it enriched. Poems, for instance, are pieces of hard craftsmanship made interesting to craftsmen in the same job, by the work put into them, and made interesting to everybody, which includes those craftsmen, by divine accidents: however taut, inevitably in order, a good poem may appear, it must be so constructed that it is wide open, at any second, to receive the accidental miracle which makes a work of craftsmanship a work of art.

5. DO YOU THINK THE STATE OR ANY OTHER INSTITUTION SHOULD DO MORE FOR WRITERS?

The State should do no more for writers than it should do for any other person who lives in it. The State should give shelter, food, warmth, etc., whether the person works for the State or not. Choice of work, and the money that comes from it, should then be free for that man; what work, what money, is his own bother.

6. ARE YOU SATISFIED WITH YOUR OWN SOLUTION OF
   THE PROBLEM AND HAVE YOU ANY SPECIFIC ADVICE
   TO GIVE TO YOUNG PEOPLE WHO WISH TO EARN
   THEIR LIVING BY WRITING?

Yes and No, or *vice versa*. My advice to young people who wish to earn their living by writing is: DO.

POETIC MANIFESTO

From *Texas Quarterly*, vol. 4, no. 4 (Winter 1961), pp. 45–53. The following are the poet's replies to five questions asked him by a research student in the summer of 1951.

You want to know why and how I first began to write poetry, and which poets or kind of poetry I was first moved and influenced by.

To answer the first part of this question, I should say I wanted to write poetry in the beginning because I had fallen in love with words. The first poems I knew were nursery rhymes, and before I could read them for myself I had come to love just the words of them, the words alone. What the words stood for, symbolised, or meant, was of very secondary importance; what mattered was the *sound* of them as I heard them for the first time on the lips of the remote and incomprehensible grown-ups who seemed, for some reason, to be living in my world. And these words were, to me, as the notes of bells, the sounds of musical instruments, the noises of wind, sea, and rain, the rattle of milk-carts, the clopping of hooves on cobbles, the fingering of branches on a window pane, might be to someone, deaf from birth, who has miraculously found his hearing. I did not care what the words said, overmuch, nor what happened to Jack & Jill & the Mother Goose rest of them; I cared for the shapes of sound that their names, and the words describing their actions, made in my ears; I cared for the colours the words cast on my eyes. I realise that I may be, as I think back all that way, romanticising my reactions to the simple and beautiful words of those pure poems; but that is all I can honestly remember, however much time might have falsified my memory. I fell in love—that is the only expression I can think of—at once, and am still at the mercy of words, though sometimes now, knowing a little of their behaviour very well, I think I can influence them slightly and have even learned to beat them now and then, which they appear to enjoy. I tumbled for words at once. And, when I began to read the nursery rhymes for myself, and, later, to read other verses and ballads, I knew that I had discovered the most important things, to me, that could be ever. There they were, seemingly lifeless, made only of black and white, but out of them, out of their own being, came love and terror and pity and pain and wonder and all the other vague abstractions that make our ephemeral lives dangerous, great, and bearable. Out of them came the gusts and grunts and hiccups and heehaws of the common fun of the earth; and though what the words meant was, in its own way, often deliciously funny enough, so much funnier seemed to me, at that almost forgotten time, the shape and shade and size and noise of the words as they hummed, strummed, jigged and galloped along. That was the time of innocence; words burst upon me, unencumbered by trivial or portentous association; words were their spring-like selves, fresh with Eden's dew, as they flew out of the air. They made their own original associations as they sprang and shone. The words, 'Ride a cock-horse to Banbury Cross', were as haunting to me, who did not know then what a cock-horse was nor cared a damn where Banbury Cross might be, as, much later, were such lines as John Donne's, 'Go and catch a falling star, Get with child a mandrake root', which also I could not understand when I first read them. And as I read more and more, and it was not all verse, by any means, my love for the real life of words increased until I knew that I must live *with* them and *in* them, always. I knew, in fact, that I must be a writer of words, and nothing else. The first thing was to feel and know their sound and substance; what I was going to do with those words, what use I was going to make of them, what I was going to *say* through them, would come later. I knew I had to know them most intimately in all their forms and moods, their ups and downs, their chops and changes, their needs and demands. (Here, I am afraid, I am beginning to talk too vaguely. I do not like writing *about* words, because then I often use bad and wrong and stale and woolly words. What I like to do is to treat words as a craftsman does his wood or stone or what-have-you, to hew, carve, mould, coil, polish and plane them into patterns, sequences, sculptures, fugues of sound

expressing some lyrical impulse, some spiritual doubt or conviction, some dimly-realised truth I must try to reach and
realise.) It was when I was very young, and just at school, that,
in my father's study, before homework that was never done, I
began to know one kind of writing from another, one kind of
goodness, one kind of badness. My first, and greatest, liberty
was that of being able to read everything and anything I cared
to. I read indiscriminately, and with my eyes hanging out. I
could never have dreamt that there were such goings-on in the
world between the covers of books, such sand-storms and ice-
blasts of words, such slashing of humbug, and humbug too, such
staggering peace, such enormous laughter, such and so many
blinding bright lights breaking across the just-awaking wits and
splashing all over the pages in a million bits and pieces all of
which were words, words, words, and each of which was alive
forever in its own delight and glory and oddity and light. (I
must try not to make these supposedly helpful notes as con-
fusing as my poems themselves.) I wrote endless imitations,
though I never thought them to be imitations but, rather,
wonderfully original things, like eggs laid by tigers. They were
imitations of anything I happened to be reading at the time:
Sir Thomas Browne, de Quincey, Henry Newbolt, the Ballads,
Blake, Baroness Orczy, Marlowe, Chums, the Imagists, the
Bible, Poe, Keats, Lawrence, Anon., and Shakespeare. A
mixed lot, as you see, and randomly remembered. I tried my
callow hand at almost every poetical form. How could I learn
the tricks of a trade unless I tried to do them myself? I learned
that the bad tricks come easily; and the good ones, which help
you to say what you think you wish to say in the most meaning-
ful, moving way, I am still learning. (But in earnest company
you must call these tricks by other names, such as technical
devices, prosodic experiments, etc.)

The writers, then, who influenced my earliest poems and
stories were, quite simply and truthfully, all the writers I was
reading at the time, and, as you see from a specimen list higher
up the page, they ranged from writers of school-boy adventure
yarns to incomparable and inimitable masters like Blake. That
is, when I began, bad writing had as much influence on my
stuff as good. The bad influences I tried to remove and renounce
bit by bit, shadow by shadow, echo by echo, through trial and

error, through delight and disgust and misgiving, as I came to
love words more and to hate the heavy hands that knocked
them about, the thick tongues that had no feel for their multi-
tudinous tastes, the dull and botching hacks who flattened them
out into a colourless and insipid paste, the pedants who made
them moribund and pompous as themselves. Let me say that
the things that first made me love language and want to work
in it and *for* it were nursery rhymes and folk tales, the Scottish
Ballads, a few lines of hymns, the most famous Bible stories and
the rhythms of the Bible, Blake's *Songs of Innocence*, and the quite
incomprehensible magical majesty and nonsense of Shakespeare
heard, read, and near-murdered in the first forms of my school.

You ask me, next, if it is true that three of the dominant
influences on my published prose and poetry are Joyce, the
Bible, and Freud. (I purposely say my 'published' prose and
poetry, as in the preceding pages I have been talking about the
primary influences upon my very first and forever unpublish-
able juvenilia.) I cannot say that I have been 'influenced' by
Joyce, whom I enormously admire and whose *Ulysses*, and
earlier stories I have read a great deal. I think this Joyce question
arose because somebody once, in print, remarked on the close-
ness of the title of my book of short stories, *Portrait of the Artist
As a Young Dog* to Joyce's title, *Portrait of the Artist as a Young
Man*. As you know, the name given to innumerable portrait
paintings by their artists is, 'Portrait of the Artist as a Young
Man'—a perfectly straightforward title. Joyce used the painting
title for the first time as the title of a literary work. I myself made
a bit of doggish fun of the *painting*-title and, of course, intended
no possible reference to Joyce. I do not think that Joyce has had
any hand at all in my writing; certainly his *Ulysses* has not. On
the other hand, I cannot deny that the shaping of some of my
Portrait stories might owe something to Joyce's stories in the
volume, *Dubliners*. But then *Dubliners* was a pioneering work in
the world of the short story, and no good storywriter since can
have failed, in some way, however little, to have benefited by it.

The Bible, I have referred to in attempting to answer your
first question. Its great stories of Noah, Jonah, Lot, Moses,
Jacob, David, Solomon and a thousand more, I had, of course,
known from very early youth; the great rhythms had rolled

over me from the Welsh pulpits; and I read, for myself, from
Job and Ecclesiastes; and the story of the New Testament is part
of my life. But I have never sat down and studied the Bible,
never consciously echoed its language, and am, in reality, as
ignorant of it as most brought-up Christians. All of the Bible
that I use in my work is remembered from childhood, and is the
common property of all who were brought up in English-speaking communities. Nowhere, indeed, in all my writing, do I use
any knowledge which is not commonplace to any literate person.
I *have* used a few difficult words in early poems, but they are easily
looked-up and were, in any case, thrown into the poems in a kind
of adolescent showing-off which I hope I have now discarded.

And that leads me to the third 'dominant influence': Sig-
mund Freud. My only acquaintance with the theories and
discoveries of Dr Freud has been through the work of novelists
who have been excited by his case-book histories, of popular
newspaper scientific-potboilers who have, I imagine, vulgarised
his work beyond recognition, and of a few modern poets,
including Auden, who have attempted to use psychoanalytical
phraseology and theory in some of their poems. I have read
only one book of Freud's, *The Interpretation of Dreams*, and do not
recall having been influenced by it in any way. Again, no honest
writer today can possibly avoid being influenced by Freud
through his pioneering work into the Unconscious and by the
influence of those discoveries on the scientific, philosophic, and
artistic work of his contemporaries: but not, by any means,
necessarily through Freud's own writing.

To your third question—Do I deliberately utilise devices of
rhyme, rhythm, and word-formation in my writing—I must, of
course, answer with an immediate, Yes. I am a painstaking,
conscientious, involved and devious craftsman in words, however unsuccessful the result so often appears, and to whatever
wrong uses I may apply my technical paraphernalia, I use
everything and anything to make my poems work and move in
the directions I want them to: old tricks, new tricks, puns,
portmanteau-words, paradox, allusion, paranomasia, para-
gram, catachresis, slang, assonantal rhymes, vowel rhymes,
sprung rhythm. Every device there is in language is there to be
used if you will. Poets have got to enjoy themselves sometimes,

and the twistings and convolutions of words, the inventions and contrivances, are all part of the joy that is part of the painful, voluntary work.

Your next question asks whether my use of combinations of words to create something new, 'in the Surrealist way', is according to a set formula or is spontaneous.

There is a confusion here, for the Surrealists' set formula was to juxtapose the unpremeditated.

Let me make it clearer if I can. The Surrealists—(that is, super-realists, or those who work *above* realism)—were a coterie of painters and writers in Paris, in the nineteen twenties, who did not believe in the conscious selection of images. To put it in another way: They were artists who were dissatisfied with both the realists—(roughly speaking, those who tried to put down in paint and words an actual representation of what they imagined to be the real world in which they lived)—and the impressionists who, roughly speaking again, were those who tried to give an impression of what they imagined to be the real world. The Surrealists wanted to dive into the subconscious mind, the mind below the conscious surface, and dig up their images from there without the aid of logic or reason, and put them down, illogically and unreasonably, in paint and words. The Surrealists affirmed that, as three quarters of the mind was submerged, it was the function of the artist to gather his material from the greatest, submerged mass of the mind rather than from that quarter of the mind which, like the tip of an iceberg, protruded from the subconscious sea. One method the Surrealists used in their poetry was to juxtapose words and images that had no rational relationship; and out of this they hoped to achieve a kind of subconscious, or dream, poetry that would be truer to the real, imaginative world of the mind, mostly submerged, than is the poetry of the conscious mind that relies upon the rational and logical relationship of ideas, objects, and images.

This is, very crudely, the credo of the Surrealists, and one with which I profoundly disagree. I do not mind from where the images of a poem are dragged up: drag them up, if you like, from the nethermost sea of the hidden self; but before they reach paper, they must go through all the rational processes of the intellect. The Surrealists, on the other hand, put their words down together on paper exactly as they emerge from chaos; they do not shape these words or put them in order; to them, chaos is the shape and order. This seems to me to be exceedingly presumptuous; the Surrealists imagine that whatever they dredge from their subconscious selves and put down in paint or in words must, essentially, be of some interest or value. I deny this. One of the arts of the poet is to make comprehensible and articulate what might emerge from subconscious sources; one of the great main uses of the intellect is to *select*, from the amorphous mass of subconscious images, those that will best further his imaginative purpose, which is to write the best poem he can.

And question five is, God help us, what is my definition of Poetry?

I, myself, do not read poetry for anything but pleasure. I read only the poems I like. This means, of course, that I have to read a lot of poems I don't like before I find the ones I do, but, when I *do* find the ones I do, then all I can say is, 'Here they are', and read them to myself for pleasure.

Read the poems you like reading. Don't bother whether they're 'important', or if they'll live. What does it matter what poetry *is*, after all? If you want a definition of poetry, say: 'Poetry is what makes me laugh or cry or yawn, what makes my toenails twinkle, what makes me want to do this or that or nothing', and let it go at that. All that matters about poetry is the enjoyment of it, however tragic it may be. All that matters is the eternal movement behind it, the vast undercurrent of human grief, folly, pretension, exaltation, or ignorance, however unlofty the intention of the poem.

You can tear a poem apart to see what makes it technically tick, and say to yourself, when the works are laid out before you, the vowels, the consonants, the rhymes or rhythms, 'Yes, this is *it*. This is why the poem moves me so. It is because of the craftsmanship.' But you're back again where you began.

You're back with the mystery of having been moved by words. The best craftsmanship always leaves holes and gaps in the works of the poem so that something that is *not* in the poem can creep, crawl, flash, or thunder in.

The joy and function of poetry is, and was, the celebration of man, which is also the celebration of God.

IDIOMS

Title supplied. Manuscript of a projected radio broadcast belonging to Mrs Edith Capon, to whom Thomas gave it in 1952, some time before leaving for his second visit to America in January of that year. Originally seven pages; the fifth page of the manuscript is missing. Square brackets denote authorial deletions.

In the opinion of most etymologists—not to be confused with entomologists, who have bees in their bonnets about insects— the 'bucket' of that phrase means the beam of wood from which pigs used to be hung, grunt upon a time, when they were about to join the great pigority. I'm not, by the way, any kind of an etymologist. And as for being an entomologist, I can hardly tell one wasp from another. I just like words. They're my vitals and my victuals. Well, these pigs, poor swine, who, oddly enough, objected to being killed, would, in their struggles, very *often* kick the bucket; metaphorically, of course, they *always* kicked it.

There are hundreds of phrases in the English language to do with 'kicking the bucket', and very understandably too, for one might say that death plays a great part in our lives. Only tax and unhappiness are as inevitable. Poets write about it all the time. (Poets, by the way, are still very romantic persons; they still want to 'get away from it all', and find a kind of heaven on earth. And what do they do? They run away to to-day's equivalent of the sea, the British Broadcasting Corporation.) Poets, when they're very young, and have just had their hearts broken for the first time, write about death with ecstatic longing; it can't come too soon for them. When they're a bit older, and their hearts have been broken so many times it's like carrying a pile of old rattling crockery around in your chest, they write about it a little more cautiously. Come, lovely death —but not quite yet, I'm busy, call tomorrow. And when they're much older, and writing, if not with one foot, at least with one syllable, in the grave, they write about death with terror and loathing as though it were something absolutely fatal. Now a man on his death-bed is faced with a great number of verbal alternatives: enough, indeed, to kill him. Shall he enter the valley of the shadow, or just conk out? Shall he give up the ghost, join his fathers, go over, pass over, go over the hill, drop off the hooks, slip his cable, shuffle off this mortal coil, or just pop off? He can be called to a better land or join the last round-up; he can hand in his checks, those ones will never bounce; he can be a landlord at last; he can croak, go phutt, go west, push up the daisies, be taken or took, or be put to bed with a shovel. One thing is certain: it's curtains for him. It's all U.P. and napoo.

Was it Bernard Shaw who said that England and America were divided by a common language? Anyway, it's that division that I like so much. [When I read popular hairy-chested American fiction, and reports in the yellow press, of hoodlum slayings and sugardaddies' lovenests, and the unfunny funnies full of cuties and supermen.] I like a durante for a nose, and schnozzles for nostrils. I like 'barefoot on the top of the head' for being bald. I like think-tank for brains and, especially, dew-beaters for feet. There's a sort of poetry in those phrases, about as subtle as a belt in the beezer with a baseball bat, but, all the same, tough and alive and inventive. And what can be lower than a snake's chin? And who can be barmier than some-one who's nutty as a fruitcake—you could put that screwball in the bughouse any day. Americans, who think, anyway, that most of the English are flat tyres and dim bulbs, blah-faced and pickle-pussed, and are always putting on the dog, say that nothing gives them a hoarser horse-laugh than to hear an Englishman try to use American slang. All his words and phrases, they say, are always hopelessly out of date. And this, of course, is because a vigorous new folk-language, such as American, changes day by day. [as soon as a wisecrack begins to grow stale in the mouth, it loses its crack; the images must always be sizzlingly, brutally new and come barking and biting out; you should be able to utter them as though you had just invented them in your own think-tank] For all I know, as a foreigner, the violent language of jiveing and jitterbugging, for

instance, is dead as a doornail now—I can't keep away from
death today—but I still like it. If you're fond of hot dancing, you
can cut, dip, peel, shag, slice, strut, stomp, swipe and swizzle,
you can kick the mule, cut a rug, gallop in the groove and jelly
the goulosh—if you're strong enough. Words I can do without
myself are eatery, beanery, filling station, eat joint, lunchery,
hashery, soupery, drugstaurant, dinnerette, nookery, eatetaria
for places where you eat. But I think the phrase for a dining-car
is brilliant: a crumb castle. And, for a very cheap café, a quick-
and-filthy has its points. [I'm indifferent about a moo-slab for
a joint of beef, but am all for]

A good, but painful, way to appreciate the paucity of one's
vocabulary of invective is to drop a heavy weight on one's toe
and then step aside and listen to oneself. The same few ugly
words, monotonously, if vehemently, repeated, with a few
blasphemacious variations will be all you'll hear. Behind you,
you have the roaring majesty of Shakespeare and the molten
wrath and thunder of Marlowe, and all you can bellow is X, Y,
Z, with a few childish frills. One method of getting children to
like poetry would be to say to them, 'Unless you learn to read
and appreciate, for example, the Elizabethans, all you'll be
able to say when some enormous disaster overwhelms you—such
as slamming your fingers in the door—are the handful of
words you're not supposed to know—you know the ones I
mean'. Haven't we all been driven half daft and corybantic by
what we imagine to be the stubborn imbecility of some one near,
dear, and beastly to ourselves? Oh, that dunderpated hoddy-
doddy, jobbernowl and jinglebrain, up to her flumadiddle, we
think to ourselves, and all we can call her is a donkey or a
goose, both excellent creatures. Someone behaves very badly to
us. Do we cry: You churl! You dragoon! You bludgeon!
cockatrice and bouser! lubber! harpy! botch and bilker!
dacoit, cootie, mumping scrip, carbuncle, brabbler, you make
me wamble? No, we call him a blanking blank. We must read
and devour more and more with our ears and eyes, roll the
words like great gobstoppers round our tongues, nourish and
cherish 'em, or we will lose our priceless heritage of elaborate
rich vituperative gnarled and resounding Billingsgate.
   The words I most dislike are those meaningless ones that I

myself use most often. Honestly is one. 'No, but honestly', I
hear myself say when I am about to tell some mild milk-and-
water lie. 'No, but honestly', when I want to emphasise some
dull and trivial point. 'No, but honestly' just to give a bit of
punch to something that isn't worth saying. A thoroughly dishonest word. And my other big dislike is 'nice'. Nice sunset,
nice pint, nice girl, nice weather, nice chap, nice poem. A
thoroughly nasty word. Well, it's been very nice gabbling on
like this and I enjoyed it. Honestly.

REVIEWS

1. From *Adelphi*, vol. 8, no. 6 (September 1934), pp. 418–20.

William Soutar, THE SOLITARY WAY.
William Montgomerie, SQUARED CIRCLE.
Sydney Salt, THIRTY PIECES.

There are the young American poets bowing down before the golden standard of Mr. Ezra Pound and his crown of green pamphlets; the hybrid young men of all nationalities publishing their smart Yankee haikus and verbal designs from Paris and Majorca; the young Englishmen conducting, in monthly and bi-monthly periodicals, a Communist agitation that fails in every instance for the reason that the Workers, for whose benefit the revolutionary ambiguities are created, can never obtain the periodicals in question and would not understand a single syllable if they did; the middle-aged English satirists looking in retrospect upon their literary death in the great war; the unburied, but equally lifeless, men of letters propped up between Sir John's large and yellow pages; the men of vision, warped by a material world, who stare like Narcissus upon their ghostly bodies or listen to the echo of their own voices in their ears. The true future of English poetry, poetry that can be pronounced and read aloud, that comes to life out of the red heart through the brain, lies in the Celtic countries where the universities are establishments for the obtaining of degrees and the instruction in school-mastering, and where the artistic coterie is no more dictatorial an affair than the local John O'London's Society or the amateur theatre. Wales, Ireland, and, in particular, Scotland, are building up, from a tradition of ballad, folk song, the pawky obscenities of Robert Burns, whom McDiarmid calls the Poet Intestinal, and a whimsical Victorian banality (the Celtic Twilight), a poetry that is as serious and as genuine as the poetry in Mr. Pound's Active Anthology and most of the poetry in Mrs. Monroe's very supine anthology is decadent and insincere.

The chief merit in the work of Mr. Soutar and Mr. Montgomerie, two Scots whose work has been encouraged by the *Adelphi*, lies in the seriousness with which they attempt to be poets all the time, not practitioners of an intellectual substitute. Mr. Soutar is not, by a long way, a satisfactory poet. It would not, perhaps, at this stage in the development of a true Celtic poetry, be a healthy sign if he were. He does not even promise that he will become more satisfactory as he develops individually, for his philosophy has gone far beyond his power of expression. His verses abound with the tricks and felicities of the dead poetry of the philosophical Wordsworth and with a prosaic inevitability of rhyme and rhythm that defeats even his occasional grace of phrasing. But his Solitary Way is the only way, and he is not frightened to take it. His philosophy is as old as the hills; it is, indeed, the philosophy of the hills which find their ultimate and rocky selfhood in their isolated contact with the rest of the living world. But Mr. Soutar writes from an inner compulsion to write poetry. At the moment he is too content to *incline* towards words and not to work *out* of them. But he is an authentic poet. His verse is dictated by his ear as well as by his creative intelligence.

'The Death of the Ear' would be an apt subtitle for a book on the plight of modern poetry. Mr. West, writing in the June *Adelphi*, did not mention the fact—a fact that must be obvious to him—that most of the work of Mr. Pound, much of Mr. Auden and Mr. Day Lewis, and the entire output of Mr. Pound's disciples, Mr. Ronald Bottral, Mr. Carlos Williams, etc., does sound abominable. It would be possible to explain this lack of aural value and this debasing of an art that is primarily dependent on the musical mingling of vowels and consonants by talking of the effect of a noisy, mechanical civilization on the delicate mechanism of the human ear. But the reason is deeper than that. Too much poetry to-day is flat on the page, a black and white thing of words created by intelligences that no longer think it necessary for a poem to be read and understood by anything but the eyes.

Mr. Montgomerie, like Mr. Soutar, is a genuine poet. His

poems can be read aloud and understood by ear and brain. His book, divided into six blank verse sections, is described as a vision of the Cairngorms. Mr. Blunden, in a quoted note, seems to regard the book as a series of poetical sermons on the problem of over-civilisation, and how to 'present the next generation with a better balanced civilisation than our own'. The same might be said of a volume by Mrs. Marie Stopes.

Mr. Montgomerie has no more individual a message than Mr. Soutar, but his diction is his own, his influences mainly those of a few carefully chosen contemporaries, and his vitality of rhythm and his preoccupation with the beauty of words two signs that promise the possible development of a poetry of the first importance.

All he writes needs firmer condensation; the images, and the natural descriptions of which he is particularly fond, need a more muscular bringing together. Thought and expression can be tightened and made more as one. Even at the present, his verse loose as it is, there can be no doubt as to his authenticity. And nearly all he writes is a pleasure to the ear.

Mr. Sydney Salt's *Thirty Pieces* are worth mentioning for one reason only. How can the Caravel Press go to the trouble of setting by hand five hundred copies of these little absurdities? Mr. Salt will never convince me that he did not write all the thirty pieces between shaving and breakfast. One piece is called, 'Poem of No Value'. This then, I gather, is a poem of value:

ALMOND ORCHARD

Snowfire,
flowerflakes,
eyes of laughing children;
riverlight,
bunched girlheads,
or just the good voice?
These are experienced trees.

It is customary, in some circles, to say that beneath the flimsy exterior of verse such as this lies the hard kernel of sense. If one did trouble to probe beneath these flimsy pieces, one would undoubtedly find that the kernel is on half-pay.

2. From *The Bookman*, vol. 87, no. 518 (November 1934), p. 132.
John Pudney, OPEN THE SKY.

Between the poetry of private subtlety and the poetry of public vitality, the devil, if you will, of escapism and the deep sea of communal contact, too many poets of this day fall into a miniature gehenna of words where even the flames that blister them are contradictory. Mr. Pudney, in his second, as in his first, book of verse is one such unfortunate, a gifted retailer of second-hand ideologies and a competent employer of the current vocabulary who is perpetually undecided as to whether he shall publicly propagate what Mr. Auden has taught him or whisper privately what he himself has experienced. Sometimes on the public platform, advocating the necessity of a pictorial bloodshed, and sometimes at the back of the hall, hiding a bag of nerves behind the electorate, he is, all the time, too conscious of his generation, of his intellectual identity with a community of intellectuals baptised in blood and hopeless as to the revival, through practical politics, of a maladjusted world. Open the sky most certainly, but the rules of property control even that imperative idealism; it must be the personal image or illusion of the sky, and the sky must be an individual symbol; too many have opened the communal sky to find some celestial Lenin there grinning over the output of the propagandist poets.

In Mr. Pudney's play, which takes up half the present volume, Mary, Joseph and the Magi enact again the scene of the revolutionary nativity. The Magi, comprising the Broker, the Mortgagee and the Ace (Gold, Property and the Crowd), explain the negative elements of their civilization in a verse that is satirically as unsubtle as it is emotionally and technically derived from Mr. Auden's Charade. On the side of positivity Joseph, the agitator, and Mary the bloody-minded mother, are, in symbolic intent, little more communist than they are fascist. Theirs, in any case, are the advocations of a rigorous hate and a purge of bad blood with the decisive stroke of the bayonet. It is probable that Mr. Pudney was unconscious of the effect he produces in his Audenesque.

His images, too, fail in their violence: 'a filthy propaganda like a cough', 'bitter as bedclothes in the morning light', 'the straining canopy of crisis'. Too great a dependence upon the short pause, the halting comma, produces in nearly every poem an intellectual and emotional stutter, so that Mr. Pudney's acute responsiveness to 'the contemporary scene' is the responsiveness of an observer with a verbal affliction.

The most satisfying poems are the title poem and the four sonnets, all of which are authentically rhythmed and worded and promise something of an original development. The two least satisfying poems are 'Forget' and 'Forgive'.

Mr. Pudney will not resent the apparent harshness of this review; he has a right to be judged by the standards he himself sets up, and those standards are very high. He is unsatisfactory only when compared with the best of contemporary poetry; it would be an insult to him if he were judged excellent by the standards of the mediocre.

3. From *New Verse*, no. 12 (December 1934), pp. 19–20.

Stephen Spender, VIENNA

There is more than poetry in poems, in that much of even the most considerable poem is unpoetical or anti-poetical, is dependent upon the wit that discovers occult resemblances in things apparently unlike or upon the intellectual consciousness of the necessity for a social conscience. In a poem, however, the poetry must come first; what negates or acts against the poem must be subjugated to the poetry which is essentially indifferent to whatever philosophy, political passion, or gang-belief it embraces. It is not our concern whether Mr. Spender moves towards the literary-political left or right, or whether he arrives; we are concerned only when the destination, left or right, is regarded as being of more importance than the method of progression. In his previous work, Mr. Spender, sensitively working from words, has arranged a well-chosen, if limited vocabulary, and expressed a sincere emotional reaction to a world that, even if it has not had its day, has at least a palpable weak end. What, in his earliest poems, was extraneous to the poetry was the unpoetry of immature sentiments. In *Vienna*, what is extraneous is the substance and the craft of the poem, both of which are anti-poetical.

Dollfuss and Fey are nice words. Does it really matter if they are, or are not, nice men? This would appear ridiculous if it were not for the fact that Mr. Spender, working now away from words, regarded only the historic significance of these two men as being important, and not the verbal context in which he placed the letters that make up their names. To many the historically emotional significance is all that matters; it may be all that matters to Mr. Spender; if so, Mr. Spender, who has forgotten the true function of poetry, would be wise to become more aware of the content of politics and revolution and to compose what would necessarily be most effective propaganda. As a poem, *Vienna* leaves much to be desired; in the first place it leaves poetry to be desired; and, in the second, any real intensity of the propagandist mission. The propaganda is bad, to be condemned, and even despised, by the real communist, whether he be intellectual or not. Here we have a revolutionary poem published by Faber and Faber, i.e. published, one supposes, without the disapproval of the author of *The Rock*, which dignified pageant was written for a church fund, blessed by a bishop, and attended by Royalty. What sort of revolutionary propaganda would Mr. Eliot permit himself to publish? Obviously not that which would have any effect, but rather that of the stand-in-the-corner, pat-on-the-back young man who, by his insistence on the crudities of language and the tin thunder of naughty images, sets himself up immediately as the communist-intellectual type, pigeon-holed by *Punch*.

Vienna is a bad poem; the images are unoriginal singly, and ambiguous, often meaningless, collectively. The sensitivity that has gone towards the making of *Vienna* is the sensitivity to mass emotion and to the emotion following upon a recital of the incidents of mass emotion; it is rarely the sensitivity to words put together, or rhythm, to the shape, substance, and sound of words. On pages 15, 19, 20, 25, 30, 37, 38, 41, and 42, and on other pages, will be found lines, passages, images, and clusters of images of a falsity and affected ugliness as uncommon to the past Mr. Spender as they are common to the present political poets to whom he lends—for how long it is still not our concern —his moral weight and literary gifts.

4. From *The Bookman*, Christmas 1934, p. 12.

Ruth Pitter, A MAD LADY'S GARLAND.
Wilfrid Gibson, FUEL.
John Lehmann, THE NOISE OF HISTORY.
Thomas Moult (ed.), THE BEST POEMS OF 1934.

Here are three volumes of individual work, and one anthology. In Miss Pitter's ironic verses a slight but genuine reputation is strengthened and, let it be hoped, made permanent; Mr. Gibson, cheerless as ever, continues doing quite well what he has been doing quite well for years; and with the publication of Mr. Lehmann's second book the worst fears as to his authenticity are realised; and Mr. Moult has once more scoured the literary periodicals of two continents with a fine disregard for merit.

Miss Pitter, a technician of brilliance, writes, for the most part, in archaic measures, and with a precision of phrase and an ornate concealment of emotion that rarefies her satire into a thing at once hard and brittle. Artificial it may be, but no more than the calculated harshness of many of the contemporary schools; Miss Pitter, unlike such invertedly conventional breakers of rhythm, is a poet (there should be some androgynous word) in spite of her artifice, and not because of it. In no instance does she parody the sixteenth or seventeenth century modes; she exploits them to their full, with little sense of the supercilious and with much inherent sympathy. Most of the present poems are concerned with the affairs of insects, reptiles, and the humbler animals. The Earwig 'that would fain sing Epithalamion' and is constrained to write Elegy is, perhaps, the most admirable comic creation. But it is difficult to pick and choose among the various excellences of the Bee Turned Anchorite, the Heretical Caterpillar, and the philosophical Coffin-Worm. Miss Pitter's is a highly original talent which must be recognised.

Mr. Gibson has been a popular poet for longer than many of us can remember. Those who respect his sincerity and conscientious workmanship will find in this latest collection the same dramatic melancholy that characterised his earlier poetical plays, the same preoccupation with the 'heartbreak in the heart of things' that has made his 'Lament' the most famous of his poems, and the same aesthetic vulgarity. In the shorter poems the straining after the moral platitude is far too obvious, but later, in the monologues and the disclosures of the senti-mental activities in a northern tenement building, Mr. Gibson, with a journalist's perception and a splendid economy of incident, comes into his own again. I am still wondering why he does not write short stories.

How much more sophisticated are the new poems and prose poems of Mr. John Lehmann. And how much less satisfying. Mr. Gibson, vulgarist as he is, is never sham; much in this latest addition to the Hogarth Living Poets is as dead as a last year's waltz, as hollow as an empty tumbler with a copy of Mr. Spender's Poems laid on the top. Mr. Lehmann, who writes a great deal from a turbulent Germany or Austria, is certainly gifted; he is sensitive to rhythm, his own and Mr. Spender's; he is often very charming in an insipid way. It is his timidity, verbal and temperamental, that prevents him from fulfilling his early promise. He never will be, as he attempts to be, a poet of the masses. A minor voiced lyrist, a soft romanticist in a hard age, he is more concerned with the tinglings of his delicate nerves than with the percussions of his own loud generation.

Mr. Moult has again selected the worst poems of the year. It is time that these dreary anthologies, having no purpose but the glorification of mediocrity, should be done away with. Antholo-gies are, at the best, pernicious to the intelligent reading of poetry; one poem sucks the blood of another; two or more similar varieties of talent are apt to cancel out; and the quantity of derivative verse must, inevitably, detract from the merit of the paucity of the original.

5. From *Adelphi*, vol. 9, no. 4 (January 1935), pp. 255–6.

M. K. Gandhi, SONGS FROM PRISON.

Songs from Prison, translations of Indian lyrics, were made in 1930 when Mr. Gandhi was in Yeravda Jail, Poona. Now, adapted for the press, with alterations in phraseology, the omission of Indian names and symbols, and the adoption of a rough-and-ready metrical form, it is difficult to estimate how

near they are to the originals of the hymns from the Vedanta
and the Bhakti literatures. Most of them are of the monistic
school of thought. The poets seek freedom and love for the
worried and apparently unworthy human spirit, for what the
sixteenth-century Tulsidas calls this 'low, corrupt and filthy,
vice-totted, anguish-racked, soul of mine' rather than the subjective truths of the Chandogya Upanishad or the Tory solu-
tions of life, the heaven for the good and the hell for the bad, of
the Rig Veda.

The present translations can do little more than supplement,
in a very small way, the work that has been published from
Oxford and Allahabad during the last fifty years. But it is a
handy little book for those who wish to have an elementary outline of Indian devotion, and Mr. Gandhi's writing, when the
hand of Mr. John S. Hoyland, the editor, has not been too
heavy in its attempts to make conventionally poetic what has
but the simplest poetry in it, is clear and unaffected.

All royalties from the sale of this book will go towards the
funds of Mr. Gandhi's work for the removal of Untouchability
in India.

6. From *Adelphi*, vol. 9, no. 5 (February 1935), pp. 312–14.

Lyle Donaghy, INTO THE LIGHT, AND OTHER POEMS.
John Lehmann, THE NOISE OF HISTORY.
Ruth Pitter, A MAD LADY'S GARLAND.

It can be said, with the utmost sympathy, that a poet should
have his bottom kicked every week. A periodical reminder of
the pain to be experienced through his immortal backside
would do much to reduce to a more proper significance the
poet's only too frequent assumption that the common flesh of
man is not his concern, and that the exhibition of his adolescent
skull swollen to the size of a coco-nut is of sufficient importance
to compensate for the little green pea of his natural talent.

That is, perhaps, an undeservedly harsh introduction to two
books of verse—Miss Pitter's literary zoopraxinoscope is
excepted—by two such obviously young men. For the sake of
their susceptibilities, let the opening paragraphs of this short

review be interpreted more as a generalisation than as a speci-
fied attack upon their work. Mr. Donaghy, nevertheless, would
be wise to indulge in a little self-brutality and, as a necessary
result, to stand upon two real legs rather than swoon upon the
bosoms of an imaginary Fanny Brawne. He has no close contact
with reality, the reality of the flesh or the spirit, of the innuendo
or the written word, of natural phenomena or the paranoic
hallucination so zealously cultivated by the continental surrealist. Mr. Donaghy himself would disagree. In his introduction he explains that his own work is in the 'integrally classical
and aristocratic' tradition of Irish poetry, 'imaginative,
achieving the universal through the particular; individual,
concrete, humanly rich, learned in craft and proudly licensed,
strict, puissant'. Mr. Donaghy likes Mr. Donaghy. His book,
beautifully produced, is divided into six sections. The first, very
lush, contains some good lines and shows a delectable appreciation of the beauty of words:

> Drowsy with surfeit of the bunched red currants,
> The blackbird hangs upon a new-stripped branch
> And see-saws, pondering the next fiery spray.

But even the Irish need a little bread-and-butter with their
poppy and mandragora. And all he gives them is another layer
of the

> . . . sweetness oozed from his lank bag
> Of clover and crushed mountain finger-bells.

The second section, 'Poetic Shapes', contains another over-
sumptuous meal of syrups, balsams, odorous spices and milky
nothings. The third section, 'Aux Rois', including a poem
entitled, 'The Superb Riot of Rhododendrons', the fourth,
'The Garden of Roses', the fifth, 'Cymbals', lusher than ever,
and the concluding, 'Into the Light', are, with their attendant
cornucopia and creams of love, altogether too much of a good
thing. What a superb riot, Mr. Donaghy.

There is a shapeless promise in this ooze of words, and a
pendulous romanticism of theme and texture, that contrasts
almost favourably with the pallid, the bogus 'modernisms' of
Mr. Lehmann's lyrics and the only half disguised whimsi-
calities of his prose-pieces. Mr. Lehmann conveys the impression

of a narrow but sensitive mentality seeking through poetry not, as he himself declares, 'the extreme attic of the mind', but the nursery of half forgotten illusions. The world, the melancholy world, even the noise of history, frustrates him. He lacks energy, as Stephen Spender lacks it. He superimposes a false vitality upon the body of a tired and a moded poetry, evading all the issues of the flesh or the spirit:

> Sometimes I'm lucky, find a key to turn,
> Open an inch or two—but always then
> A bell rings, someone calls, or cries of fire
> Arrest my hand when nothing's known or seen
> And running down the stairs again I mourn.

When Mr. Lehmann writes from Berlin or Vienna, he adopts a sympathetic attitude towards the workers of those shirted capitals, but perceives more of the refracted preciosities of a generation deprived of its libertarian manhood than the blasphemies inherent in the forces for evil that effect that deprivation. A mournful ghost of 'a world that has had its day', he moves through the Nazi scene sensitive to the echoes of the voices of the despairing poor; but his occasional fervours— 'Save us from the slow poison of closing factories, of the mud that oozes through the cracks in our shoes, and the familiar journey to the pawnshop'—are no more than the fashionable compensatory fervours of a pseudo-poetic defeatism, which will be on the side of the proletariat or be damned. Mr. Lehmann is found to be an expert assimilator of current rhythms. He never suggests that he is working towards the solidification of an individual symbolism, imagery, mythology. Some of his poems will taste very nice to the casual sampler of contemporary verse; to me, at least, they leave in the mouth the faint, contradictory flavours of aerated water and marzipan.

But now, with Miss Pitter, we approach the fringes of a world that is more permanent. She has created her own symbols, as Mr. Lehmann has not; as Mr. Donaghy has not, she has tautened the forms of her verse and built up a cold armour of irony around the warm centres, sharpened each single epithet and, with the extremest skill, employed a deliberate archaism of method that suggests neither the eighteenth century peg in the twentieth century hole (compare the Sitwells) nor the pretty peg that has no hat hung on it (compare any of our mannered professional litterateurs). Here in her insectarium are the sorry scrawny flies, the green brethren of the caterpillars; here is the armed earwig who swanked in his mail, the snug dame Ladybird in scarlet brave, the leaden louse, the buxom sheep-tick, safe in the wool. Here, too, is the pious lady trout, the wistful-headed frog, the bee turned anchorite, the matron cat with her,

> Purra wurra, purra wurra, pronkum pronkum;
> Purra wurra pronkum, pronkum purr.

These are her symbols, informed with the irony and the classical imagination that draws out of all their movements the subtlest grotesques of human behaviour. It is the coffin-worm ('which consider') who ends this strange book:

> We and our generation shall sow love
> Throughout the frame he was not master of.

Miss Pitter is mistress of the frame of her verse. Unlike so many suckling favourites of the moment who begin to disintegrate the content of their poetry before there is any content there, she has solidified her ironic abstractions into a content as concrete as it is supple. She is, primarily, a worker in words, a woman employed upon a job. It is unfortunate that so many of her colleagues in the business of poetry live on the dole.

7. From *Adelphi*, vol. 9, no. 5 (February 1935), pp. 317–18.

Alfred Hy. Haffenden, DICTATOR IN FREEDOM, TRACT FOUR.

Mr. Middleton Murry has commented, in a review of the three tracts previous to the *Dictator in Freedom*, on Mr. Haffenden's affinities with Blake and Lawrence.

Lawrence is hard to find. He was primarily concerned with the achievement of a pagan content. There is no pagan literature. The brains of man cannot lead his body to a pagan nirvana. The body has got to get there first. Lawrence tried to get to the nirvana through the androgynous and sexless body of words. His literature is the recording of an individual struggle towards a state of bliss, the Brahman ananda of the Upanishads, from which there is no literature. The birth of what he desired would have come with a literary suicide. Mr. Haffenden is anarchist. His tract is the individual recording of a communal struggle towards the state of Christhood in which the 'sovran law', the law of libertarian love, is fulfilled. He does not propose to attempt to reach this fulfilment in any of Lawrence's capitalist bunny-warrens, but through the communism, the spiritual immediacy, of the Christ in man. The state of pagan bliss produces nothing but pagan children, a brood contented with the social purpose of any civilization so long as their hot and seedy streams do not dry up. The state of Christhood produces a love-dictated progeny and a communal art.

The Blake of the Prophetic Books is not so hard to find. But the Blake in Mr. Haffenden's tracts is the prophet without his symbolism, the mystic without his poetry. Much of the Prophetic Books reads like Tupper after absinthe. The importance of Blake lies in the importance of his poetry and his monstrous mythology, not in his borrowed Judaisms. He lives because he could put words together well. He lives because he had a glorious vocabulary, a divine enquiry, the key to the files of a mystic Rogues' Gallery, and possibly epileptic vision. He does not live because he was a wise man, a man with a message, a constructive philosopher, another Mr. Middleton Murry without Mr. Murry's common sense. Possibly he was. But if he had been that and nothing much else, the Marriage of Heaven and Hell would be as little read to-day as the Divine Love and Wisdom of Swedenborg. Now Mr. Haffenden has affinities with only one side of Blake, and, as he does attempt to be a poet, it is unfortunate that it is with the less poetical side. He has yet to form his sermons into the stuff of poetry. A lot more of the living Blake and a little less Pastor Jeffries, a condescension to the laws of euphony and the essential of rhythm, and a vigorous refusal to employ again the ornamentations of phrase and symbol that clutter up the pages like the yellowing texts on the walls of an otherwise hygienic workroom—and the future dictatorial tracts will do much towards making Mr. Haffenden's Testament of Love as sensibly a poetical 'message' as any of this century.

But the unqualified generalisations, the higher-case abstractions, and all the phrases that reek of the garden-city New Jerusalem Society must go. Mr. Haffenden must read more and read deeper, clean up his diction, and forget the hyphen. He must learn, not through the protests of reviewers, but through the literature of the mind of Europe that is, to him, the teacher of all tribes and the enshriner of Complete Humanhood, that poetry which is written for 'all time' is written in and out of its own time. His message is of the twentieth century for the twentieth century, and his expression an ambiguous mixture of the styles of any century but this. There must be no compromise. His living message must be made in living language. Let him read Yeats and Rilke, reach his phrasing independently, and have no fear of the blue pencil. The struggle is there, the rhetoric is there, and the vital pinch of fanaticism.

The tract costs one shilling. A 'message of new birth and the secrets by which the desires and hopes of life are fulfilled, a vision of a man, a society, a world at one with itself',—for the price of a large Player's.

8. From *Adelphi*, vol. 10. no. 3 (June 1935), pp. 179–81.

J. W. Tibble (ed.), THE POEMS OF JOHN CLARE.

Here, in these two solid and well-produced volumes, Mr. J. W. Tibble, author of the standard biography of Clare, has come near to completing the work that Mr. Edmund Blunden and Mr. Alan Porter began fifteen years ago. The poems in the 1920 edition were selected chiefly from manuscript, while the 'Madrigals and Chronicles' of 1924 consisted entirely of unpublished poems. To these, and to the majority of the works published in Clare's lifetime and after his death, Mr. Tibble has added three hundred poems from the original manuscripts. And, even so, there still remain in manuscript, according to the lucid introduction, poems considerably outnumbering all those included in the present edition. Clare was prolific enough to be condemned, even to-day, as an incorrigible versifier who rhymed from habit rather than from impulse, and who attempted to deaden the minor irritations of monotony and the horrors of a lunatic existence by chronicling the most trivial incidents and activities of the Northamptonshire countryside. He was untutored, uncritical enough to borrow indiscriminately from many of his fashionable and inferior contemporaries; to adopt the mannerisms and artifices of a current sentimentality foreign to his own attitude, an attitude towards poetry and life, towards both in one, that had the outward innocence of the peasant and the inward awareness and subtleties of an understanding genius; to allow his visual imagery and visionary powers to be obscured by the sheer weight and number of minute objective observations that were so often derived, not from the centre substance of the poems but from the edges of an uncontrolled facility for rhyme and rhythm. All this, and more, must be admitted, if the quality of the true John Clare, the self-consumer of his woes, the chronicler of the shifting seasons and the changing, changeless, country scene, the lover of all women in the image of his unfulfilled first love, shall be lastingly determined among the various qualities of Shelley, Keats, Hood, Beddoes, and Darley.

It is not the purpose of this short review even to attempt to assess his historical and poetical importance. (It would be well to read Mr. Middleton Murry's essay on Clare, which is the best there is.) Whether he would have been a better poet had he been a less humble man, and whether the patronage he was accorded in his lifetime was the result more of curiosity, of an impertinent interest in the activities of a peasant with literary leanings, than of charitable intentions, those who read his life and his self-revealing poetry can determine themselves. He was an intimate poet, having little or none of the ecstasies and flourishes of an invalid romanticism; content with visible shapes and objective meanings, he did not question the natural world; he did not attempt to measure its mysteries by a hand-ruled philosophy, to work, through what would inevitably have been confused metaphysics, towards a solution of the unhappy state of mind that had shuttered him from society and forced upon him for companions the abstraction of a shadow and the inadequate concreteness of words. What is remarkable, under these conditions, is that the best of Clare becomes both social and universal poetry, and that, even at his worst, he had none of the private, masturbatory preoccupation of the compulsive egoist. To Clare the writing of poetry was an action. Poetry, to too many, is a mental accident, or a substitute for physical expression. And, though Clare's physical life was bounded, for the most part, by the walls of an asylum, he was an 'active' poet, just as Keats, despite his enduring passion, was a man who acted life through poetry. Though words were his active medium, Clare worked towards them, not out of them, describing and cataloguing the objects that met his eyes. In the beginning was the object, not the word. He could not realise, and consequently his expression suffered, that the word is the object.

> I loved, but woman fell away;
> I hid me from her faded flame.
> I snatched the sun's eternal ray
> And wrote till earth was but a name.

This, in spite of the apparent contradiction in the fourth line, is a good example of how Clare was conscious only of the secondary intensity of words. The 'faded flame' and the 'eternal ray' he had encountered many times in the little poetry he had read and appreciated; he gives these worn phrases an individual meaning only because of his innocent and entirely sincere appropriation of them to describe what he himself had felt and wished to express. Language to him was rarely more than a vehicle, often somebody else's, to carry along an individual body of feeling and incident.

The best of Clare is to be seen in the sequences of sonnets written in Northborough asylum between the years 1832 and 1837, and in the slight lyrics and love songs. He imitated Crabbe, Burns, and Cowper, but he did it badly; his Miltonic echoes were pompous enough, but the circumstances never merited them; his introspective poems, even allowing for the few magnificent lines in 'I am', and the hitherto unknown poem following it in Mr. Tibble's edition, do not show to the full his particular quality of loving understanding and the peculiar hard edges and ancient curves of his diction.

> Love lives beyond
> The tomb, the earth, the flowers, and the dew.
> I love the fond,
> The faithful, and the true.

This was his testament.

9. From *Adelphi*, vol. 11, no. 1 (October 1935), pp. 58–9.

R. D. Jameson, A COMPARISON OF LITERATURES.

Professor Jameson's survey ranges from the experience of literature, and an enquiry into the nature of racial inspiration, to a detailed analysis of the literatures of England, France, Germany, and America. His main conclusions are that the French are concerned with problems of behaviour interpreted psychologically; that the Germans have been chiefly concerned with dreams about God and the mystery of the universe; and that English literature, a hybrid growth deriving from both French and German, and having a dual nature, stands somewhere between the two contrasting types of phantasy. Emphasis is laid upon the importance of two particular problems: the function of language in the history of literature, and the need for a more adequate notation for qualities of feeling. The function of language, it is explained, is not only completely misunderstood, it is ignored with 'blithe gaiety'. One of the reasons is that language has been surrendered by the critics into the hands of the professional linguists. Shelley was linguistically incompetent, and his poetry will be more justly appreciated, Professor Jameson believes, when this limitation is realised.

Those accustomed to the dialectic method will find a degree of novelty in the method adopted throughout this book, and, indeed, in the attitude behind it, although economic determinants of literary phases are not so much emphasised as implied. Literature is looked upon as a way of escape, the canalising of energies which should, properly, be utilised in contemporary social activities; American literature is consequently less rich than European, for Americans have been so busy living and doing, they have not required the emotional vent of words; from Irving and Bryant down to Lewis and Mencken, who suggested that it was possible to be an American and still be intelligent, they have apologised to the majority for their interest in such an unsocial phenomenon.

The experience of literature is associated with the emotional reaction towards words, and those who have the greatest need for this experience are those who labour under emotional tensions of various kinds. Periods of intense verbal activity coincide with periods of great national activity. The emotional ferment is too active to be restricted within the boundaries of environment, and flows over into phantasy.

Traditional criticism has regarded the aesthetic approach towards literature as apart from the functional approach towards the way of words; languages themselves intensify the differences which appear in literature, but languages and literatures are not two different phenomena, but the same phenomenon.

Professor Jameson takes rather a long time to say this.

10. From *Light and Dark*, vol. 1, no. 2 (March 1937), pp. 27, 29.

Djuna Barnes, NIGHTWOOD.

There should be two reviews of this book, and both written with the intention of selling it: the first to attract the intellectual flippitygibbits, who read everything new and nasty so long as a few accepted new and nasties have read it before; and one to attract by quotation, the honest people who like beautiful writing. The first review should say what an evil book it is, that it's about homosexuality, and that it's very bawdy; also that Mr. Eliot, certainly not new or nasty, has written an enthusiastic preface to the American edition. This review for the chi-chi people could have any sort of title like 'A Bible of Evil', could describe the principal character, a gargantuan doctor with a lot of surrealist club-room stories, as a symbol of utter degradation made utterly wise; it could comment on the fact that, as far as evil goes, the characters of the American, Miss Kay Boyle—with whom Miss Barnes has been compared—represent a little girl's conception of Paris. And it would sell a hundred copies in Cambridge.

The Second review is, I think, this review. 'Nightwood' was turned down by every publisher in America. It can't be called a novel, because it only has a sort-of-a-plot; the characters don't as in the actual life of fiction, develop and change from mood to mood, sentence, etcetera; they talk witty, passionate dialogues on dirty mountaintops (making, that is, the comparative unimportance of the fact of level dirt into a mountainous truth). It isn't a lah-de-dah prose poem, because it's about what

some very real human people feel, think, and do. It's 'Nightwood', by Djuna Barnes, and one of the three great prose
books ever written by a woman.

'She saw in you that fearful eye that would make her a target
forever.'

'She prayed, and her prayer was monstrous, because in it
there was no margin left for damnation or forgiveness.'

'"Well, I went off under London Bridge and what should I
see? A Tuppenny Upright! and do you know what a Tuppenny
Upright might be? A Tuppenny is an old-time girl, and London
Bridge is her last stand, as the last stand for a *grue* is Marseilles,
if she doesn't happen to have enough pocket money to get to
Singapore. For tuppence, an upright is all anyone can expect.
They used to walk along slowly, all ruffles and rags, with big
terror hats on them, a pin stuck over the eye and slap up
through the crown, half their shadows on the ground, and the
other half crawling along the wall beside them; ladies of the
haute sewer taking their last stroll, sauntering on their last
Rotten Row, going slowly along in the dark, holding up their
badgered flounces, or standing still, silent and as indifferent as
the dead, as if they were thinking of better days, or waiting for
something that they had been promised when they were little
girls; their poor damned dresses falling away over the rump, all
gathers and braid, like a Crusader's mount, with all the
trappings gone sideways with misery."'

'"Strange, I had never seen the Baronin in this light before",
the Baron was saying, and he crossed his knees. "If I should try
to put it into words, I mean how I did see her it would be
incomprehensible, for the simple reason that I find that I never
did have a really clear idea of her at any time. I had an image
of her, but that is not the same thing. An image is a stop the
mind makes between uncertainties. I had gathered, of course, a
good deal from you, and later, after she went away, from others,
but this only strengthened my confusion. The more we learn of
a person, the less we know. It does not, for instance, help me to
know anything of *Chartres* above the fact that it possesses a
cathedral, unless I have lived in *Chartres* and so keep the relative
heights of the cathedral and the lives of its population in proportion. Otherwise it would only confuse me to learn that Jean
of that city stood his wife upright in a well; the moment I

visualize this, the deed will measure as high as the building; just as children who have a little knowledge of life, will draw a man and a barn on the same scale.'''

And so many more quotations which there isn't any room for.

11. From *Time and Tide*, 9 October 1937, p. 1328.

Martha Dickinson and Alfred Leete Hampson (ed.), THE POEMS OF EMILY DICKINSON; *Edna St. Vincent Millay*, CONVERSATION AT MIDNIGHT.

Emily Dickinson was born in Amherst, Massachusetts, in 1830, and lived there in seclusion until 1886, the year of her death. The first selection of her poems was published in 1890, and two further selections appeared shortly afterwards; another volume, *The Single Hound*, was published in 1914, and the *Life and Letters* in 1924; later there was a collected edition of her poems, thought then to be complete; this was followed by the publication of *Further Poems* in 1929, and *Unpublished Poems* in 1935. In this present edition, all the poems of the preceding collections, just over 900 in number, are included in a single volume. Emily Dickinson, who published little or nothing in her lifetime, who scorned success, who was secret and exultant in the creation of her private world and the cultivation of her eccentricities, and whose poems, in their neat, tied packages, were entries in a sentimental diary, notes against the world, and voucher tickets for Eternity, has become an idolized exhibit in American literature. She did not need appreciation when she lived, was proof against conviction or conversion, and is now accorded a blind, worthless worship. She is placed 'indubitably and permanently among the enduring poets of the English-speaking race'; her gnomic imagery is praised for its 'tremendous implication'.

At its best the poetry is a curiosity, the curiosity of a narrow abstract vision interpreted in legal, commercial, financial, and mathematical phraseology, furnished with the objective commonplaces of a life lived between the sewing basket and the bird bath, the Bible and the account book; for the most part, her poems are the result of a single impulse, and become but isolated pieces of experience; her worst is Stitch-and-Wilcox translated into a literary pidgin-English. She was, Mr. Hampson writes in his introduction, 'primarily interested not in form, but in what she had to say'. It is as sensible to remark that she was primarily interested not in words, but in ideas, and as ludicrous to forget that, in all real poetry, the idea, the word and the form are inseparable. Emily Dickinson had only two methods of making a poem: one was to record a single experience, draw a moral from it, or pin a moral on it, and the other was to put down the moral without the experience. Sometimes she combined the two methods by concluding the record of an experience with an independent moral. And when the experience she wished to communicate had a visual origin, she made a word-picture of it; a word-picture is not poetry at all, being created towards words and not out of them. Her messages, her dazzling communications, are few and simple. She said, in 900 different metaphors, in hymnal quatrains, in contorted syntax, in language borrowed from ledger, text book, and knitted text, with a distinguished absence of aural sensitivity, with studied archness, natural aridity, epigram, enigma, and occasional austerity, with one ear for the music of the spheres and one for the tradesman's knock, that distant terrors diminish as they approach, that the riches of the earth are incomparable to the riches of heaven, that death knows no class distinction, that the anticipation of pleasure is more pleasant than its realization, that man wants butter on his bread, and that the point about Eternity is that it goes on all the time. She possessed the power of minute, natural observation, a keen sense of paradox, and a small but authentic lyric talent. If she had been content to cultivate these, rather than her tendency towards moral platitude and her ability to fire off, on every possible occasion, wisecracks about Immortality and the higher-case abstractions, she might have deserved a little of the wildest praise bestowed upon her by those militant American litterateurs who, always on the look-out for a major public poet, are always forced in the end to accept a minor private one.

Conversation at Midnight is a play to be performed in the mind, but not in mine. The reader himself must invest the speakers with dramatic character and give them movement. All the speakers have the same voice and use the same vocabulary. They are, in turns, facetious, precious, pompous and dogmatic.

In lyrics, sonnets and free verse they discuss politics, religion, love, sport, and literature. The dialogue is dramatically ineffective, the poetry negligible, and the arguments are inconclusive. It is a distressing thought, but Miss Millay is so widely and earnestly read in America she may yet have every club bore speaking her language.

12. From *New English Weekly*, vol. 12, no. 23 (March 1938), pp. 454–5.

Samuel Beckett, MURPHY.
William Carlos Williams, LIFE ALONG THE PASSAIC RIVER.

It is easy, flippant, and correct to say that Mr. Samuel Beckett —whose first, very imitative novel, 'More Pricks than Kicks', I remember more by Joyce than chance—has not yet thrown off the influence of those writers who have made 'Transition' their permanent resting-place. But Mr. Beckett, who is a great leg-puller and an enemy of obviousness, would hate to be reviewed by the cash-register system that deals in the currency of petty facts and penny praises, so if I do not straightforwardly praise his new book 'Murphy', for its obvious qualities—of energy, hilarity, irony, and comic invention—then it is his fault: he should never try to sell his bluffs over the double counter. I must say that 'Murphy' is difficult, serious and wrong.

It is difficult because it is written in a style that attempts to make up for its general verbosity by the difficulty of the words and phrases it uses for the sake of particular economy, and because the story never quite knows whether it is being told objectively from the inside of its characters or subjectively from the outside. It is serious because it is, mainly, the study of a complex and oddly tragic character who cannot reconcile the unreality of the seen world with the reality of the unseen, and who, through scorn and neglect of 'normal' society, drifts into the society of the certified abnormal in his search for 'a little world'. Murphy is the individual ostrich in the mass-produced desert.

I call the book wrong for many reasons. It is not rightly what it should be, that is what Mr. Beckett intended it to be: a story about the conflict between the inside and the outsides of certain curious people. It fails in its purpose because the minds and the bodies of these characters are almost utterly without relation to each other. The Dublin Professor, whose mental adventures and adventurous conversations are loud and lively and boisterous, is a slap-stick, a stuffed guy, when he moves; his mind is Mr. Beckett's mind, and is full of surprises, but his figure is that of the taped and typed 'eccentric professor' of music-hall and cartoon. The Dublin tart talks furiously and excessively, with a vocabulary like a drunken don's; the street bookie can speak like this in a pub, 'The syndrome known as life is too diffuse to admit of palliation. For every symptom that is eased, another is made worse. The horse leech's daughter is a closed system. Her quantum of wantum cannot vary'; but tart and bookie are no more than walking, gesticulating brains, and the story fails because no-one can care at all what happens to their bodies. And much of the book is loosely written; 'The imperturbable negligence of Providence to provide money goaded them to such transports as West Brompton had not known since the Earl's Court Exhibition', for instance.

The story begins in London, and progresses through a conventional Dublin, where every tart is a crank and every pub-bore a self-starter, to a series of obscure events in lunatic-asylums and lodging-houses that might have been created by P. G. Wodehouse, Dickens, and Eugene Jolas working in bewildered collaboration. Mr. Beckett supposes that he writes about the lowest strata of society, about the dispossessed and the regardless-of-possession, but he takes a most romantic view of it; he looks generously at the dregs, and makes every dirty, empty tankard wink at the brim; romantically he searches in the gutter for splendour and, in every fool and villain he finds, substitutes the gunpowder brain for the heart of gold.

And, lastly, Mr. Beckett's humour, for the book is packed with it even in the most serious sections and the most pathological discussions. Sometimes the humour is like that of an Irish comic journalist forced to write in an advanced Paris-American quarterly, sometimes like that of an old-fashioned music-hall character-comedian attempting to alter his act for a pornographers' club. And always it is Freudian blarney: Sodom and Begorrah.

I know that Dr. William Carlos Williams has a great reputation in America, built up like a pack of visiting cards, that he is boosted by Pound and turns up like a penny in almost every American culture-expert's periodical and anthology, that no new literary movement can hope to succeed without the benefit of his name or an example of his typography, and that he is the nearest American approach to Mr. Herbert Read. But I did not know, until I read his new collection of stories, 'Life Along the Passaic River', that he was such a tough boy; he takes his sentences by the ears and treats them rough, putting one over on the deputy-Master of the Faber hounds who is still patting his syntax and giving lumps of sugar to his prose. Dr. Williams has a practice in an industrial town, and most of these stories are, plainly, medical cases told in that slang-strung, hard boiled, manly manner that is derived, in most instances, from a pretentious fear of being called literary, pansy, or soft-centred: 'Aw, can it, I'm no Shelley, I'm just an ordinary guy.' Accuse a fifth-form public-schoolboy of writing secret sonnets, and you get the same reactions. Dr. Williams dumps down little colourless word-bricks in every sentence, dispenses entirely with atmosphere, description, characterisation, and even form; understating emotions, he giggles with embarrassment at the least suggestion of tears or kisses, or he shouts with embarrassed defiance. Many of these stories read like contributions to the Gangsters' Lancet: 'I made the examination and found the head high but the cervix fully dilated. Oh yeah.' But all of them are told with an honesty and anger—for Dr. Williams's patients come from the tenement slums and the foul, unnecessary plague-holes of polyglot, American poverty—that the affected *and* insipid convention of trying to write like an enemy of writing cannot hide or subdue.

13. From *New English Weekly*, vol. 13, no. 2 (April 1938), pp. 34–5.

Eric Ambler, EPITAPH FOR A SPY.
Sheila Radice, NOT ALL SLEEP.

The life of a spy, in any of Mr. Oppenheim's or Mr. Le Queux's cosmopolitan fairy tales, is as exciting, romantic, and chivalrous as that of a police officer in any of the innumerable adventures of Wallace in Wonderland. The wicked Buchaneers of those dull but sterling spy stories that always begin in a Scotch mist are model gentlemen; the spies of my acquaintance who put their ears to diplomatic keyholes or steal the plans of the invisible ray or sell their country's honour to a man with twelve nationalities and no shame in a Budapest drinking den, always seem to smile and shrug their shoulders, with a 'Well, it's all in the game', as wearily and whimsically as Mr. Herbert Marshall on the films sacrificing his life for a flag or a skirt. It has been realised, lately, by a few writers, English Anthony Berkeley, for instance, and American McCabe, that the detective story—the story where all is Knox above the belt, which has at least two murders and four suspects, which lays out its clues fairly, which introduces no Chinamen, secret passages, missing wills or marriage licences, holy relics stolen from Eastern tombs, or supernatural agencies—has reached a last, sterile point of efficiency; more than new tricks are needed to save the detective story from a lengthy suicide, more than new variations on the old theme of 'who did it', more than new types of detectives, and certainly more than Style. It has been realised that all the cramping rules must be broken, that the ideas of good taste and clean play must be done away with, that the day of the individual detective, good or bad, official, unofficial, dictatorial, noncommittal, painstaking, lackadaisical, intuitive, scientific, is over: Holmes, Thorndyke, Poirot, Hanaud, Wimsey, Fortune, Carrados, Travers, Sheringham, Masters, Wolfe, Storey, French, Carter, Pointer, Vance, Mason, Mayo. Death in the library, the houseparty, or the sealed room, has been done to death; the surprise has gone out of the surprising discovery that the murderer is, as one expected, the last person one would expect; we know too well the first person, or Ackroyd, murderer, and we have grown tired of the kind of story that begins, 'On December 25th I decided to kill auntie.' Just as the straight modern novel needs formal tightening— (and to tighten form is not to garotte syntax like Miss Stein; to condense language is to compress it concertinawise like Joyce; to make prose economical is not to make it starve, like Hemingway's, of essentials; at least a quarter of most straight modern novels is, because of the dictatorial demands of publishers as to the length a novel must be, just padding)—so the modern detective story should be formally loosened up. To the devil and the Book Clubs with rules and good taste; let the detection, if necessary, be wild and woolly, the clues be faked or withheld, the red herrings be whales and, as a final insult to the conventions, let the murderer turn out to be, on the last page, an entire stranger who hasn't appeared in the story at all. (I am indebted to Mr. Cyril Connolly for this last suggestion.) That the detective story has become smug and self-satisfied, is being realised slowly, and a few writers are attempting to liberate it and to use what is, basically, a very fine medium, with humour, experimental violence, and no respect. (I should like here to recommend, to anybody fed up with the usual sort of mechanical crime-fiction, a book which came out a few years ago but which attracted too little attention: Lawrence Vail's, 'Murder! Murder!')

But the spy story is little more advanced today than it was when 'The Riddle of the Sands' was written; and Somerset Maugham's 'Ashenden', which was wise entertainment and showed up espionage as a shabby, undignified business with no glory or romance, seems to have been unread, or misread, by those writers who make their heroic spies—*i.e.*, on 'our side'— a mixture of Bulldog and Pimpernel, and their villainous spies, their anarchists or armament manufacturers, mere professional devils without life or sense. This being so, it is with unexpected pleasure that I can congratulate Mr. Eric Ambler on his sensible, subtle, exciting and witty, 'Epitaph For A Spy' which is the best book of its kind I have read since 'Ashenden'; the communist agent in it is a living and faithful man, not a bad joke with a bomb in its beard; there is pity in it, and terror; and it is very well written.

'Not All Sleep' is a curious book, and I never really knew what was going on in it; people appeared to be moving and loving in a veiled and decorated prose through an oblique world, but the reason was mysterious to me; all the action seemed to take place in a half-light, and the scenery to be always in shadow. The story is about James Hammond, the very little known 18th century poet; and I don't know much more about him now. Mrs. Radice is very familiar with her period, but sometimes seems to think that her readers are, too. There are several brilliant scenes, and much graceful incidental phrase-making. But everything is seen through a period glass, and the characters move darkly, like ghosts, in a papery dusk.

14. From *New English Weekly*, vol. 14, no. 6 (November 1938), pp.
92–3.

H. G. Wells, APROPOS OF DOLORES.
Rose Wilder Lane, FREE LAND.
Jane Allen, I LOST MY GIRLISH LAUGHTER.
Signe Toksvig, PORT OF REFUGE.

Who can guess, after each new voluminous, curious, digressive,
annoying novel, the shape of Wells to come? He has grown up in
the words of ideas, and his magnificent vitality of invention
increases with age. His habit of swallowing the English language
whole still disagrees with him too often, and words like 'De-
Dolorefication' rise windily up. To my generation, brought up
in a land fit for Neroes to live in, now suddenly adult, forced by
fashion to a Fascist or Communist declaration, he has become
a familiar, but misunderstood, bogey: the militant, *unromantic*
individualist. He has been called Fascist by advanced caption-
readers: a clear case of label. To many, he is a Red who dyed.
But so many of the severest critics of one of the most widely-
read, circulated, and Pollyglot authors in the world today have
failed to read him. To them, Mr. Wells's new novels are just an
annual vent. But this particular book, titled with all his famous
lack of Taste, vehemently overwritten, unashamedly and, often,
boastfully erotic—death to the decorated sexual Morgan and
the Flashing Streamers!—should shake up anyone not absurdly
prejudiced against good story-telling and independently
adventurous thinking. It is the story, in the form of her very
intelligent husband's journal and diary, of the married life and
death of a superlatively common woman: common to the nth,
and described under the third, degree. The complications of
human relationships, the inner wars, the shocking nervous
frictions, the ulterior savageries, are handled expertly and
coarsely; the pedant's nagging forefinger gives place to the
thumb-at-nose; he bullies the gentle emotions like a fishporter;
he lectures over his sexual impulses as though they were newts
in bottles; there is always the urchin in the biologist; Mr. Wells
is a rather different specimen of the boy who never grows up; a
sort of Peter Bedpan. He is badtempered as ever over people he
does not like; his distortions have the ring of truth, even if it is

only a nose-ring by which he leads his characters to the vivi-section chamber. The publishers of this book state that the last scene is an imaginary meeting with Dolores in another world; this other world must have required another kind of print, for the scene does not appear. But the terrestial end contains some of the finest reflective pages that Mr. Wells has written.

'Free Land' is another novel of American pioneering. Its popularity has been compared to that of 'Gone With The Wind Into 20 Editions'. All the worst people recommend it. The 'Times' Lit. Sup. says it has 'a quiet touch of poetry', and who should know less about it? Quite incidentally—which means, in this case, quite on its own merits—it is a grand book, broad and moving, violent and dignified, the story of the almost unendurable heroism, blindness and superb stupidity, of simple people asking little in terrifying weathers. Compared with this, the storms of most recent fiction blow in teacups on Foyle's luncheon table. The wind blows a baby 11 miles. In a snow-buried sledge a newly-married pair lie close together and eat sugar and snow. Frostbite is taken as calmly as toothache or childbearing. Put your feet in the oven, when you're in agony there's no danger. The horrors of such pioneer living appear at their highest in the small domestic details, and in the silent, almost genteel, starvation; they are intensified the more they become ludicrous. 'What say we have a glass of vinegar and water,' says a man when he learns that his wife is going to have a baby, 'this calls for celebration.'

'I Lost My Girlish Laughter' is a crazy story about Holly-wood. By crazy I don't mean Marx or Ritz but the Anita Loos, Peggy Joyce tradition of inconsequent, gold-digging, girlish gossip and tough but coy cracks about sex said by girls with bee-stung lips; New Yorker stuff now that the New Yorker has gone whimsical and tame. The truth is crazy, and the fault of Miss Jane Allen's book is that it is not true enough. She intro-duces the trivial pretence of a romantic plot with two more-or-less ordinary people in it—ordinary not by Hollywood's standards—as an attempt to make lifelike and to put in a worldly perspective the incredible life of a cock-eyed world. Far better for her to have exaggerated what was already fan-tastic, than to try to tidy up with a giggle.

Naomi, heroine of 'Port of Refuge', is a small Swede with a

psychic flow who works in an American factory counting collar tabs. She goes into trances while counting, and imagines herself, mostly naked, on the Swedish dunes. This proves bad for her health, and she is made a collar paster. Later, through influence, she rises to a button-holer. After working on collars for so long, it's no wonder she's a pain in the neck. This leads to a job in an office where she falls for the boss's son. And when she falls, she falls; she wants and writhes and suffers; desire bores at her nerves like a Swedish drill; when she looks at the quirk in his upper lip she feels 'like a small iron filing before a magnet'. After pages of passionate strife—'surely the caverns of Alph themselves could not hold all the feelings she had poured out'—she is married to him. This is not as good as she expected. Still wanting like anything, she falls for the vicar; he likes her, too, but she writes him such a letter that he becomes a Trappist monk. The story ends with Naomi looking in a mirror and not seeing her reflection. Is she dead or is she a vampire? It is no exaggeration to say that Miss Signe Toksvig can write.

15. From *New English Weekly*, vol. 14, no. 17 (February 1939), pp. 256-7.

John Dos Passos, u.s.a.

Franz Kafka, america.

'U.S.A.' is three novels in one: '42nd Parallel', '1919', and 'Big Money'. It is a monstrously efficient and depressing, vigorous and sordid, continent of facts. It is the uncondensed material for the Great American Novel, that ton of a dry dream which has ruined beyond repair such a number of ambitious men. It is a collection of newspaper headlines, lines of popular songs, potted biographies, political speeches, impressionist snippets, documentary Marches of Time, cinema captions, talkie dialogue, debunking propaganda, sociological research, and huge slabs of tireless, tiring narrative written in many styles but always toughly, always with coarse penetration and loud subtlety. Explorers into the great wastes, jungles, cities, pitfalls and sugarpits of the G.A.N. have usually been small men who should have stayed working, according to their natures, on a kitchen garden, an orchid bed, a sewer farm or a window box. John Dos Passos is the only contemporary American novelist I know of whose journalistic abilities, whose memory and concentration, sympathies and energies, general information, intensity of purpose, and knowledge of the turbulent order of the world he lives in, were strong and broad enough to assure the success of his inevitable failure in attempting to put his continent in a book. But, in presenting every side without side or exaggeration, in reducing nearly all activities to a level of social hopelessness, in refusing to stress, by whatever means, the value of one thing, whatever that thing might be, over the value of another—sex, drink, patriotism, snobbery, despair, ambition, corruption, for example all seem to be treated in the same way, to be given the same strength of attention—Dos Passos is bound to miss truth and produce monotony, to make his necessarily coloured world one dull shade of you know what kind of brown. 'U.S.A.' is too long, of course; nearly every novel is; novelists still believe, quite rightly and dishonestly, that their readers can be carried along, uncomplaining, by the mere mechanics of prose, over large passages of unlightened tedium that go to make the required number of words, just as poets think that they can write as many mechanical lines of verse as their laziness dictates or allows if only there is a strong line of poetry further on or further back to compensate for them; there are other reasons, too: a bore's best club is his novel, and he can make it the size of an armchair. Each of the three novels in 'U.S.A.' has the same impressive formal plan, and the same curious, now hackneyed, system of section-headings, meant to make one think that the whole work was grandly conceived and carried out according to strict conceptions. I am one who does not think that. The impressive plan covers all accidents. Anything can happen, from verbosity to affected naiveté, and the rigid structure opens, like a bolstered bosom, to let it in.

To the stern admirers of Franz Kafka, it will appear cheap and, almost, irreligious to include this first admirable English translation of one of his most admired novels as just another of the just remembered books of a dead year packed with unconvincing successes and equally unconvincing failures. (The 'books for the few' were written by members of a few groups of few people, and their quality was dictated by a mass-minded minority.) But a 'dream-fragment'—as a lot of people describe any unformed book which can't keep up to its intentions, which is so often meant to impress by the exciting possibilities of what the gaps and omissions might contain if the author had got over his arrogant incompetence and querulous laziness—can only be a bit of a book. 'America' has a beginning and a tail, no middle and no sting. The theme, as in all his bits of books, is that of the imperfection of all human action, of the external encourage-ment of action and its parallel circumvention of the freedom, the inevitability, and the eternal error of all human choice. He minimises the quantity of hope to a *certain* suspicion of helpless-ness, yet manages at the same time to extend its quality; all the circumstantial details he describes of the vigorously dubious, hole-hearted objective world are contradictions of despair; one despair is created by the sense of the unalterable solidity of facts; facts, to Kafka, were the beginnings of undoing, and he tried to undo them all. It's no good saying what a book 'America' might have been if Kafka had made it into a book; we must take the fact of 'America' as it is, full of expected surprises and suspicious truths—truths, that is, with inward-staring, unbelieving eyes. In his introduction Edwin Muir, who with Willa Muir made the translation, says, 'There seems to be a necessity in the gaps which are left in the stories; if he had filled up these gaps, others would have appeared.' There must, apparently, always be a hole in Kafka's stories to keep them together. But if insertion in one place forces displacement in another, then, surely, either the stories, as objective containers, are too small or the material is lumpy, unconcentrated. I needn't tell what this story's about, admirers will read it any-way. It's a far more comic and, straightforwardly, delightful story than The Castle or The Trial, although it has many passages of sinister ambiguity and many intangible horrors solidly observed, the fateful allegory is less insistent, there is even the suggestion of a happy ending—an ending, no doubt, which would have been the beginning of doubt; but Kafka's figures still move about in the bottom of a well, treading water slowly with a desperate and innocent dignity. And I think 'America' is the least permanent of all his stories because, so much more than the others, it relies on the surprises of an eccentric charm, and charm has a very long death.

16. From *New English Weekly*, vol. 15, no. 5 (May 1939), pp. 79–80.

Flann O'Brien, AT SWIM-TWO-BIRDS.
Ruthven Todd, OVER THE MOUNTAIN.
Erskine Caldwell, JOURNEYMAN.

I am told that the reviews of novels in intelligent weeklies should be written for people who are not going to read the novels, which means that the reviews themselves have got to be good reading and whether the novels are or not is a matter to be settled between the author, his God, and his publisher. In fact, the worse the novels the brighter the reviews, for praise is empty and irritating to those who are not going to look at the praised object while condemnation of the work of others is always appreciated. When novices' bits are labelled masterpieces every other Sunday by best-smellers, when Guff the poet praises Puff because Huff, who is Puff's poof, reviews verse in 'Burgeon', 'Nine', 'Object', 'The Sixpenny Verse Stores', 'The Urban Heap', 'Dodo', or 'Isthmus'—there's no need now to describe all the well-known rackets and pulled strings, or to count the balls—how many readers of this column would believe me if I said that 'At Swim-Two-Birds' was a great novel? (It isn't, and I'm not saying so.) What does the reader want from the reviewer? A summary of each book, so that he won't be caught out if the books are talked about? Stars, percentages? An article on the Novel, full of the names of other people, with the new books dragged in at the end as illustrations or warnings? ('Mr. O'Brien's novel has not the plangent force and spiritual hunger of Dostoievsky's. Neither has Mr. Todd's. Both fail.') Let me try to mix up this small review in several popular ways. I give 'At Swim-Two-Birds' 75 per cent. and four stars. It is an attempt—and could be subtitled 'Blarney's End' for it is hard to think that any ordinary Irish writer who uses the kind of materials Mr. O'Brien so vigorously and imaginatively destroys could, after reading it, produce anything but the parody of a parody—to tumble together all the ingredients of Irish litera-ture, legend, ballad, Twilight, pub and lower-class Dublin, etc., into one broth of a story. Throughout the book passages of autobiographical reminiscence written with elaborate facetious-ness and winking pomp, mock-grand circumlocution, interrupt, often to elucidate, often to bewilder further with numbers of devices turned on their heads and elucidation pulled inside out, the magnificently comic and moving incursions into mythology, the eccentric progenitive and obstetric adventures of Mr. Trellis, a sinning publican and novelist, the admirably shady and shadily respectable conversations of Mr. Trellis's characters who conduct their own lives outside his action when he is asleep and perpetuate their lives by the secret administration of sleeping drugs, the lovely narrative of mad King Sweeney the birdman, the plots, counterplots, that are, with little continuity and no obvious plan, for fun and tricks' sake, fitted, cheek to impudence, dignity to whimsy, into this extravagant but Highly Recommended fantasy. The influences of Dunsany and James Stephens are as strong as the publicised influences of Sterne and Joyce. This is just the book to give to your sister, if she's a loud, dirty, boozy girl. It does not possess the acute sensitiveness of Mrs. Virginia Woolf. I have read a better book. What Mr. O'Brien will bring out next is nobody's business (he could, I believe, become a great comic writer), but this alone establishes him in the forefront of contemporary Irish literature among several others whose names I cannot at the moment remember.

Mr. Ruthven Tood, in his first published novel, has carefully selected the writers whom he thinks he should be influenced by. When he forgets his self-imposed indebtedness to 'recent classics', and is not awed into pretentious symbolism and shabbily surrealist dream descriptions, he writes with charm. A nice, natural vulgarity breaks down the false good taste. But the story, which tells of the adventures of a vicar's son who climbs the Pale Peak and descends into an unknown, Fascist nightmare country the other side, is unsuccessful because, as soon as it gets going, as soon as there's plenty of rapid action and grotesque melodrama, the author remembers that he is supposed to be a serious writer and immediately brings in his undigested influences, precious poetical sentences, naive propaganda. If only he would turn a deaf ear to unnecessarily advanced advice, and poke a rude tongue at fashionable literature, he could write an entertaining and thrilling story. 'Over the Mountain' has, by the way, the worst cover I've seen on any novel this year, a peak of blancmange, a white bird, a purple star, an uplifted face, expressing perfectly all the more annoying nonsenses of the book itself.

I delayed my notice of Mr. Erskine Caldwell's doggone comedy, 'Journeyman', published a little time ago, in the hope that I could appreciate it more if I let it linger on in my memory. It did not linger, and, rereading it, I find again that it is not a bit as amusing as those drawings in 'Esquire' in which bearded, lanky Southern Americans sit grumbling into their jugs of corn and observing to each other that Grandpaw has once more retired for the winter to the W.C. It's all about an itinerant lay preacher who came to drive the devil out of a lazy little town in the Southern States, in Mr. Faulkner's tough, time-perplexed, and crazy country, and who steals and soaks and lies and leches before he drives away himself. But I wished it had those 'Esquire illustrations'; it's a bare book without some point.

17. From *New English Weekly*, vol. 16, no. 9 (December 1939), pp. 133–5.

Frederic Prokosch, NIGHT OF THE POOR.
Dorothy Parker, HERE LIES.
Georg Kaiser, A VILLA IN SICILY.

I, too, have had occasion to sleep under the blanket of the stars, in the country, among the dispossessed of a city, among the disappointed provincial seekers of gold pavements, the misfits and chuckouts; and when prosperity returned, I would attempt, in warmth and comfort again, to write stories about the poor I had slept, talked, and shivered with. These stories were always false. I turned the miserable people I had met into eccentric animals of the romantic night, made anarchical gods and monsters of the ordinary but penniless men and women who longed only for respectability and a cup of tea, found startling, bounding philosophers, too big for this narrow world, in the levelling gutter where only the tired, inarticulate, rut-minded and sensibly hopeless very poor had been. Mr. Prokosch's poetic novel, neither novel nor poetry, is about the beautiful, terrible poor, the dignity of outlawry, the wisdom of the man-made wilderness; it is false, trivial, woolly, mawkish, and, for what that is worth, beautifully written. I could forgive him the grand manners, the long, mostly meaningless passages about sounds and smells, the hop dip and wallow in the exotic vocabulary of geography, his flower catalogues, his weather forecasts, but I'm not to be caught by his posh aggrandisement of nomadism, with or without a 'socially aware' commentary. I'm not going to weep over that old union. The grandeur of poverty, with or without indignation at the fact that it is grand, is as dead an idea as gypsies, as mucked and trodden as the tavern-fans' rolling road, thick with novelists' bones, grown over with leaves of grass. The story is of a boy's journey from Wisconsin to Texas, and America comes to death before you in a rich, sprawling peasoup cloud of metaphors; all the details of scent, shape, sound and colour, that Mr. Prokosch laboriously sets down in often exquisite language, make, in the end, a clot through which you can see nothing, of America or of the world, but one writer writing. As a record of things that happened to that boy, the story is absurd: dummy philosophical hoboes, out-size fantastic hitch-hikers, brooding, sexual giants with curly chests and sea-blue eyes, consumptive boys tottering straight out of Dickens, 'characters' of all kinds, litter his word-choked path and speak to him *exactly* like the rubbishy figures in any picaresque book. The journey is supposed to show the spiritual growth of this sensitive, ordinary boy, but all his emotions and reactions are those of an extraordinarily self-conscious, adult, talented practising poet called Prokosch. There is no growth in the boy: he begins and ends as the word Tom in a cluster of images, and the exaggerated figures of the romanticised Poor are introduced, one by one, on to the hugely over-decorated and embroidered scene to preach, patter—'Only the poor folks really know what it means to be big-hearted and to have someone else be big-hearted to you'—and do their stuff around him. I don't misunderstand Mr. Prokosch's implied indignation with the system which drives its jobless young men on to the road; I realise that he is describing, in the experiences of these wanderers and remnants of the pioneer spirit, the growth of a new disease and unrest. But I do think also that, by the drugging beauty of his prose and the emotional mis-directions and lovely muddles of motive and characterization into which it leads him, he turns this aimless wandering into an heroic, almost a holy, journey, which by its nature it cannot be. This straggling nomadism is not a glorious cure but a small, significant part of the ignoble illness itself. This Mr. Prokosch knows, but he writes his knowledge away. Give him a couple of pages and his adjective-bucket and he'd turn a hunger march— in spite of all his strenuous attempts to make it tough in a soft language—into a Delius-like walk through a paradise garden.

Miss Dorothy Parker, the popular American legend and well-known cat about town, has collected in 'Here Lies' all the stories she wishes to be forgotten by, and the English reader who knows only her reputation for reputation-pricking and the devastating dirty crack—'The House Beautiful', she reviewed in one line after the first night of Channing Pollock's dramatic failure, 'is The Play Lousy'—and who has read only stories about her in Alexander Woollcott's chestnut-anthology, 'While Rome Burns', can have the pleasure of becoming acquainted with as bright, silly, unpleasant, lost and pathetic a lot of people as were ever undressed and mentally molested in public. Here are stories, sketches, and monologues of all kinds and cruelties, and Miss Parker gets her talents into a surprising variety of types. From isolated stories of hers that I had read in magazines, I imagined her to be a one-track writer with one trick—the ability to turn the most commonplace, repetitive dialogue into stinging and sensitive analysis of feebly vicious character. But she can write as well (and without condescension) about 'good', dull women as about the young things, Loos legged and moralled, who try all their time to live up to the hangovers they were born with, and the bewildered, clucking matrons immortalised every week for a moment or two in Helen Hopkinson's drawings in the 'New Yorker', and the emancipated Millay-browed young women who know their place—anywhere except the kitchen or the bed. She knows her women upside down, from toe to head, from corn to dandruff or pedicure to perm. And in the story of the blind black child and the old dress-coat his begging grandmother was fobbed off with by (as Charles Morgan would say) a hypocritical con-science-smoother, she pulls the heart-strings as neatly and deftly as she plucks an eyebrow. Indeed, reading through the stories carefully—not just whizzing through them, as I did first, on the

lookout for wisecracks and a nasty laugh—you can see that a
very warm heart and a coy, almost maidenly mind dwell
beneath that glittering exterior, as old-fashioned as mothballs
or horsehairs concealed in a steel and glass chair. She's not
spite, pure spite all through, there's a mellow steak. I doubt
whether often she really means much harm. She dips her pen
in acid-drops. And phrases such as, 'her hands like heavy lilies
in a languid breeze' occur every witty page or so. Miss Parker,
to adapt one of her own criticisms, runs the whole gamut of
emotions, from A sharp to B flat.

I imagine 'A Villa In Sicily', by a distinguished Liberal-
minded German dramatist now living in Switzerland, to have
been written about 1920, though neither the publisher nor the
translator, Mr. Wills Thomas, gives any clue. It is in the form
of an intimate letter from a young Russian ex-officer, who has
assumed, for the most perplexing and unlikely reasons, the
identity of a dead waiter, to his ex-wife whom he has recently
waited on at table but who, maddeningly and improbably,
never recognised him. I couldn't understand at all why he
behaved as he did, and the predicaments his mixture of sense-
less military idealism and lugubrious apathy got him into are
not made any clearer or any more entertaining by the expres-
sionist technique Kaiser uses throughout. It's all rather like an
early advanced film: rain falling heavily between each ill-lit
shot, close-ups of faces desperately unhappy about something not
explained, portentous but apparently irrelevant captions about
the nothingness or somethingness of the earth or the soul. The
book ends, I believe, with the principal character about to go to
sea as a stoker. Or it may be that he was about to go to hell. Or
he may have been dead all the time. Nobody would know, and
perhaps that's the charm.

18. From the *Observer*, 16 December 1951.

Roy Campbell, LIGHT ON A DARK HORSE.

In the first half of this often beautiful and always bee-loud
autobiography, Roy Campbell writes of his young, blazing days
in young Durban and the African wilds; and out of the clamour
and colour and violence and enormous loyalties of those days,

out of that fantastic world of hippos and lily-trotters, flamingoes and lions, mambas and koodoo bulls and cloud-born aloes, comes much of his fiery, flowered, percussive, venomous, boasting and devoted poetry.

He spent his childhood—and very appropriately, too, for one who was to become such a vivid and unstinting figure—in a big house overspread by a fig tree full of golden-weaver birds, surrounded by jacarandas and flamboyants, flame-trees and palms. (Not roses, for Roy Campbell, but flamboyants all the way.) Here, the exotic vegetation, the unlikely birds and beasts and reptiles, the sweltering scents and sharp dry dazzles, the meat and meaning, of his unmade poems, moved wonderfully alive all about him, waiting for the relentless rhymes. Here he learnt guns and horses, fish, deer, and octopuses, the dialects of Africans and birds; he learnt to axe wild beehives, an art he introduced, later, into literary London.

His first distinct memory was that of seeing *Lwandhla*, the Zulu name for the sea, through the legs of a horse; and he remembers the lories bursting 'into the clear blue air like a salvo of green-and-crimson rockets on a dark night, crackling and sizzling with electric fire'. He killed a stag with his hands, and teased baboons, and played with scorpions, and shot great thundering beasts from the hip like the Poet Laureate of the 'Wide World' magazine.

It was a simple life, as far as any is simple, in which he grew roaring up to bulldoze through wars and opinions and print, brutal but never mean, and one where comradeship—though perhaps this word is tinged, for him, with an infernal political implication—is held extremely high. The whole family of the Campbells was zealous, industrious, quixotic, faithful, noisy and kind, and their always welcome guests were a splendidly odd lot: from the Strongest Man in the World, who could pick up two elephants, and his wife, who was stronger than he was, to an English professor who wanted, for some reason, the foetus of an aardvark.

All these pages devoted to Campbell's early adventures, triumphs and (not nearly so often) disasters, in Natal and Rhodesia, are brilliant in patches, striped and lustred with exquisite natural descriptions, grisly and grotesque with tall bush stories that almost confer on Campbell the honorary rank of B.B.C. Commander; and, for the most part, the political prejudices snap out from the kennels of brackets like cross dogs. His was not an upbringing to encourage either cowardice or modesty, and certainly Roy Campbell has neither; and there is a kind of grandeur in the way he limelights, so garishly, both his great gifts and his plain, extraordinary cussedness. But in the second half of the book, especially in the chapters about Bohemian London and his private life, those prejudiced dogs come snarling from their kennels and worry the marrow out of every bone in sight. The Spanish pages, and 'The Coming of the Terror', should be left for the consideration of another reviewer.

I acclaim the first twelve chapters, written by a poet of genius. But, for much of the rest, I think it throws rather a bad light on an old war-horse.

19. From the *Observer*, 6 July 1952.

Amos Tutuola, THE PALM-WINE DRINKARD.

This is the brief, thronged, grisly and bewitching story, or series of stories, written in young English by a West African, about the journey of an expert and devoted palm-wine drinkard through a nightmare of indescribable adventures, all simply and carefully described, in the spirit-bristling bush. From the age of ten he drank 225 kegs a day, and wished to do nothing else; he knew what was good for him, it was just what the witch-doctor ordered. But when his tapster fell from a tree and died, and as, naturally, he himself 'did not satisfy with water as with palm-wine', he set out to search for the tapster in Deads' Town.

This was the devil—or, rather, the many devils—of a way off, and among those creatures, dubiously alive, whom he encountered, were an image with two long breasts with deep eyes; a female cream image; a quarter-of-a-mile-long total stranger with no head, feet or hands, but one large eye on his topmost; an unsoothing something with floodlight eyes, big as a hippopotamus but walking upright; animals cold as ice and hairy as sandpaper, who breathed very hot steam and sounded like church bells; and a 'beautiful complete gentleman' who, as he went through the forest, returned the hired parts of his body to their owners, at the same time paying rentage, and soon became a full-bodied gentleman reduced to skull.

Luckily, the drinkard found a fine wife on his travels, and she bore him a child from her thumb; but the child turned out to be abnormal, a pyromaniac, a smasher to death of domestic animals, and a bigger drinkard than its father, who was forced to burn it to ashes. And out of the ashes appeared a half-bodied child, talking with a 'lower voice like a telephone'. (There are many other convenient features of modern civilized life that crop up in the black and ancient midst of these fierce folk legends, including bombs and aeroplanes, high-heel shoes, cameras, cigarettes, guns, broken bottles, policemen.) There is, later, one harmonious interlude in the Faithfull-Mother's house, or magical, technicolour night-club, in a tree that takes photographs; and one beautiful moment of rejoicing, when Drum, Song, and Dance, three tree fellows, perform upon themselves, and the dead arise, and the animals, snakes, and spirits of the bush dance together. But mostly it's hard and haunted going until the drinkard and his wife reach Deads' Town, meet the tapster, and, clutching his gift of a miraculous, all-providing Egg, are hounded out of the town by dead babies. (Here the sinister chapter heading is: 'None of The Deads Too Young to Assault.')

The writing is nearly always terse and direct, strong, wry, flat and savoury; the big, and often comic, terrors are as near and understandable as the numerous small details of price, size, and number; and nothing is too prodigious or too trivial to put down in this tall, devilish story.